MW00857203

THE FINER THINGS CLUB

The Summertime Chronicles
of a Yellowstone Housekeeping Employee

BY
LAUREN ERICKSON

MUSE
LITERARY

CHICAGO·NEW YORK·PARIS·ROME

Printed in the United States of America

Hardcover ISBN: 978-1-958714-95-9
Paperback ISBN: 978-1-958714-96-6
Ebook ISBN: 978-1-958714-97-3
Library of Congress Control Number: 2023934512

Muse Literary
3319 N. Cicero Avenue
Chicago, IL 60641-9998

For my dad, who not only taught me
how to camp, hike, canoe, garden, start a fire,
and make an egg sandwich but also to experience
the finer things in life.

"I went to Wyoming, in other words,
to make a man of myself."
Elizabeth Gilbert, *The Last American Man*

*   *   *

"Here is your country. Cherish these natural
wonders, cherish the natural resources, cherish the
history and romance as sacred heritage, for your
children and your children's children. Do not let
selfish men or greedy interests skin your country of
its beauty, its riches, or its romance."
Theodore Roosevelt

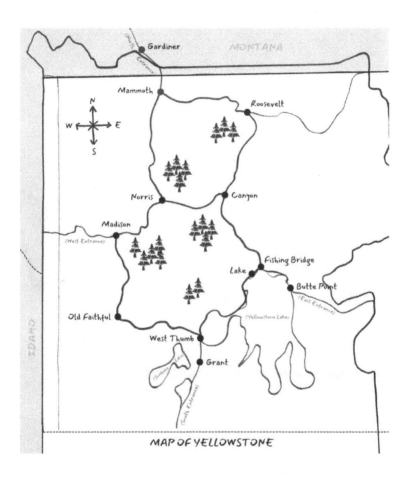

MAP OF YELLOWSTONE

MAP OF LAKE

(Yellowstone Lake)

SEASON I

CHAPTER 1

·⋅⋆◆⋆⋅·

I found myself crunched between fourteen people I'd only known for three months, posing for one last picture. I knew it'd be the last time we'd be together for what would most likely be a very long time—if ever again. We agreed to coordinate by wearing our matching imitation-Patagonia pullovers, deemed "jerseys" as if we were a competitive sports team. We might as well have been; we'd seen one another in just about every way we could—sweating against the incline of a forty-five-degree mountain, cursing under our breath while arms-deep in toilets or dishwashing soap, stumbling through the employee pub, staring starstruck at the exposed Milky Way, clutching our stomachs in laughter in our crummy little dorms...

While smiling for that picture, genuinely smiling, I couldn't help but feel something that I rarely ever felt. I was... *proud* of myself.

Every fireplace in the lodge was filled with the warm glow of reddish light. The effect was something I now thought of as *home*. In a matter of months, the simplest ingredients— trees, sunlight, mountains, fresh air—had compensated for my inner deficiencies and *I* made it happen. I took a chance when I left my Midwestern home at just twenty years old to travel over thirteen hundred miles to the most remote location in the continental US, and then do it all over again a second time. It was, in fact, my higher sense of self that enabled me to become the person I always knew I could be but was afraid to personify—the *real* me.

Thing is, I've always been sensitive, constantly feeling everything everywhere all at once in every shape and form, even as a child. Feeling "too sensitive" can be tricky; you realize early on that it can both burn and cure, break and heal, and believe that, because it's a contradiction, it must be wrong. It doesn't make sense. No one talks about it (or if they do, it's often misunderstood or misrepresented).

People like that are sometimes called chameleons because they learn to blend in—they absorb their atmosphere and take it everywhere with them. Chameleons are not allowed to drop it; they can abandon, disguise, or distract it, but never forget it.

I remember a girl in first grade who liked to swipe extra copies of worksheets from our classroom's recycle bin to play teacher with during after-school care. Each day, she instructed whatever group of kids she could manage to rally (usually no more than three) to read the directions aloud with her and begin solving math problems before walking around and monitoring our answers like a real teacher. If we had a question, we raised our hand. If we had to go to the bathroom, we raised our hand. I always felt kind of bad for her because she could never get as many volunteers as she would have liked. Everyone else wanted to play games, color, talk, or dance to whatever Kidz Bop music was playing through the stereo, but I stayed back to do her schoolwork so she would feel better. Truth is, I never wanted to. I didn't want to play the student and sit on the floor of the cafeteria and solve math problems, but I did it so she wouldn't feel let down. I wanted her to feel empowered by us calling her *Miss Ashley*, so I sacrificed my own comfort every day to fulfill her goals.

Over the course of my life, I had become fluent in reading people well enough to detect what they needed so I could more readily offer my support. It took me the better part of two decades to realize I did it all for *acceptance*. I would become everyone and me at the same time, perpetually caught in the in-between, belonging everywhere and nowhere.

I was eight when I discovered journaling. Most of the time it was about the drama of school or who had a crush on whom but, even then, I knew my journal was a safe place to make those admissions. By the time I was twenty-one I had accumulated nearly twenty of them, the contents evolving from crushes to important college decisions and onward to my first existential crisis. The quiet expectancy of a blank page always made me feel like I could tell it the truth, so I did. Over and over. For thirteen years.

Often, carrying myself through my own life felt like carrying a dandelion through a windstorm of others' opinions and expectations, and I never knew how to protect that delicate part of me until I learned the obvious: I was allowed to take shelter.

That's when Yellowstone happened.

CHAPTER 2

···◆◆◆◆···

I was driving east on Highway 90, still two hours from the park, when I broke down sobbing, snot and tears rolling down my face like fat drops of rain on a window. The thought of living and working in Yellowstone was enough to overwhelm me with anxiety and an existential fear of the unknown. I had no connections in Wyoming and knew virtually nothing about housekeeping, apart from occasional trips to my grandma's house from my college dorm for free laundry and food. All I knew was how to go to class, take tests, and scout for jobs. Tomorrow would be the first day of the next three months of my life, and it'd be the longest I'd ever been away from home, from everything I'd buried myself in for so long.

Six months earlier, before the start of my sophomore year, I was reading on the back porch of my family's home in the sweltering Missouri heat, when I received a lecture from my dad on the importance of finding a summer job.

"I told you," I reasoned, despite my growing irritation, "the library doesn't have much work in the summer and it's a forty-five-minute commute from here. The dorms are closed too, unless you want to pay three thousand for me to stay there, and they're not even that nice."

"Find something local, Lauren," he said, standing by the back door of the porch, drenched in sweat and dirt from the early afternoon yard work he'd occupied himself with.

Easier said than done. "Dad, I've already reached out to four places and haven't heard back from them. Plus, by the time I get accepted, it'll take a week or two to get trained with whatever it is, and even then, I'll only be there for a month or two."

"Follow up with them. Reach out. Ask about the status of your application. Take the initiative."

Take the initiative. He didn't know how much anxiety fueled the opportunities I *had* taken the initiative with—personal athletic records, orchestra concerts, piano competitions, a 4.0 GPA, graduating with honors, scholarships, collegiate enrollment. Whatever it might be, I always acted out of fear. Fear and the need for acceptance were what drove my accomplishments—not wanting them for their own sake. And then, in the heat of the summer and our disagreement, I got an idea. "What if I worked in Yellowstone next year?"

"Yellowstone?" He seemed surprised.

"Yeah. You did that, didn't you?"

My dad nodded. "I did. I worked in housekeeping in my twenties. Had to've been back in the eighties."

"So why don't I do that next year?"

I could see the gears in his head turning before he ultimately agreed. "You know, I think that's a pretty good idea. And you know what, if you do end up working there, I've got a bunch of camping gear you can take with you."

I nodded, grateful to be relieved of the immediate pressure and now intrigued by the thought of working there. I didn't know why I hadn't thought of it before. I'd heard plenty of his stories and he'd always spoken of them so fondly, so I knew that suggesting Yellowstone invited minimal resistance. And the more I thought about it, the more I realized it would solve three problems: (1) It would make up for my lack of employment now if I didn't get hired last-minute. (2) It would resonate deeply with my dad, thus diffusing any hesitation around it. And (3) I could do something by myself for the first time in my life.

I considered the possibility of doing something that I wanted, to taste a bit of freedom from who I portrayed and allowed myself to be—pristine, uncomplicated, and agreeable. Though that begged the question: why did I only feel comfortable doing what my parents themselves had done before? I started cross-country in seventh grade because my dad grew up running. I pushed myself into debate freshman year of high school because my mom told me how much she enjoyed it when she was my age. I planned to become a teacher because my whole family was made of them. I always had their support, especially with that, so when news broke that I'd be spending May through August working as a housekeeper in the middle of Yellowstone, just a few months after that sweltering conversation with my dad, I was—for the first time—met with silence, hesitation, worry, and fear, emotions I made a point to avoid at all costs.

Part of me felt like I had ruined my extended family's perception of me by making a choice to do something new and different, and that weighed on me. But now that I was here, driving toward the next three months of my summer, I didn't know what to expect or who I would become; I was afraid of being my own ideal, of the real me who would emerge from the false persona I had sheltered behind for so long.

As much as it scared me, I knew this was the time to take risks. I had always wondered what it would be like to be all of myself all at the same time without fear or reservation. Now I had the opportunity to find out. After all these years, who really *was* I?

From the driver's seat, my face sticky with drying tears, I stared ahead down the straight Montana highway, unblinking and meditating on these feelings of intimidation, uncertainty, and even a smidgeon of auspiciousness. I occasionally glanced at the clusters of pronghorns prancing up and down their golden hills with their signature white butts and long, curved antlers. Some stood looking out at the vast mountainous prairie before them, like kings on their thrones surveying their land. I wanted to be one of them, at least for a while, grazing, dancing, and feeling the warmth of the sunlight melting into my back.

Instead, I straightened up, sniffling myself back into place, and turned on the radio in search of a decent station.

The only direction left now was forward.

CHAPTER 3

·· ◆ ◆ ◆ ◆ ··

The next morning, I woke up in the world's most expensive Super 8 motel in a small, old-Western town in southern Montana named Gardiner. It was home to fewer than a thousand people and claimed no more than a two-mile-diameter of territory with just one main road and a giant blue stream running through it, two parallel threads running through a medallion-colored cloth. The north Yellowstone entrance stood approximately one mile from my pillow.

My nerves, relentless and unwavering, followed me all the way up to the "Employees Only" gate of the park where I checked in and received my housekeeping uniform at ten in the morning: two shirts and two pants to last me the entire summer. The button on one of the pants was hanging onto its last thread and the shirt, old and worn with a slight tear in the front pocket, was a hideous, faded pattern of blue and white vertical stripes. I waited a few extra seconds at the counter to offer the lady who issued me them the opportunity to realize her mistake and give me a fresh set, but I was instead met with a screech: "Neeext!"

I felt dazed. I wasn't present and only followed the immediate instructions I was given. *Keep your employee ID in your wallet. Get your uniform from that building. Use this map to*

find Human Resources in Lake Village where you'll be working.
I understood without substance and defaulted to following
directions. I'd always been good at that.

Driving down Grand Loop Road, the only major road in
the park, I couldn't help thinking how different Yellowstone
was compared to home. Conifers, quaking aspens, and
cottonwood claimed their land, whereas cornfields and gas
stations claimed mine. Their needles, sharp and evergreen,
saturated the air inside my car with an aromatic pine in the
same way fresh asphalt from road construction on the highway
used to. I drove like this for a while, deep in reflection of the
ways in which my two worlds were colliding, when the music
coming from my phone stopped, pulling me out of my trance.

Confused, I looked at my phone, mounted on the dashboard,
only to see that the GPS feature had gone completely blank.

What the heck?

With one hand on the wheel and partial attention to the
road, I typed Lake Village's name into the search bar again and
again, only for it to continue canceling its route computation.
I continued looking up and around only to see no further signs
or directions. Just a simple, two-lane road.

I had lost all access to the internet.

I slowed down enough to flip through the ruffle of
documents in the passenger seat next to me for the map I had
been handed. It was on a pink sheet of paper and hand-drawn
in Sharpie, clearly a copy of the original, given its extra dark
shadowing, and was my only hope of finding Lake Village.
Unfortunately, that map, as hard as it was to decipher, only
included neighborhood-specific roads.

I wasn't going to let myself panic, attractive though the
idea was. I reasoned instead. *The good news is that I know*

where I am and where I'm going. All I need to do is keep looking for signs.

Coming up to a bend in the road, I noticed something tall and brown near the gravel shoulder. I leaned into the steering wheel and squinted my eyes in hopes of making it easier to identify before pressing down on the accelerator slightly more to reach it faster. Gradually, it began to take shape and looked almost a little...*ovular.*

Huh, I thought. *That's an odd-looking sign.*

I was getting closer and closer to it, anxious to reach it and hoping it would be readable enough from a distance so I wouldn't miss any immediate turns. Then, the shape began to take the form of something different. Immediately recognizing what it was, I gasped before hitting the brakes and screeching to a halt in the middle of the road, praying I wouldn't hit it.

It was a grizzly bear. I had stopped no more than twenty feet in front of a *grizzly bear.* I knew they existed in the park, but I figured they lived deep in the bowels of the forests, not on the shoulder of Grand Loop Road. I sat wide-eyed and helpless in my car, hoping I hadn't accidentally provoked him in some way by screeching to a stop.

He hobbled across the road, seemingly unphased by this near collision. From a distance, he seemed as calm as a cloud, drifting by, not minding one way or the other what I did. But I knew better. One look at his three-inch talons and I knew he could rip me apart in a matter of seconds if he wanted to. I knew this was a time for common sense, even if he didn't seem outwardly threatened.

I remained still, paralyzed by his potential. Glancing into both my rearview and side mirrors, I saw nobody else was around. Just me. Being the only witness to a five-hundred-pound beast, living and breathing in front of my car in the middle of Yellowstone, was both terrifying and thrilling. I'd never experienced another surprise as momentous as this. It was a first.

The grizzly had made it two-thirds of the way across the road when cars began to stack up behind me. When they realized why I had stopped in the middle of the road, people began to buzz like flies in a flurry of excitement. Cameras and phones spilled out of every window in an attempt to capture the perfect shot like a flurry of paparazzi; that bear might as well have been Kim Kardashian.

He eventually moved on, carting the last of his body through the branches and twigs, until the thick brushes of pine absorbed him completely, leaving everyone in a state of awe. One at a time, the tourists retreated to the safety of their seats, sharing photographs and gushing about what they had just witnessed.

I studied the margins of the road before deciding to proceed forward, wary of any cubs that might've been trailing along behind their parent. No other animals emerged, so I remained cautious as I began picking up speed again, inch by inch on my speedometer, eventually resting at a steady forty-five miles an hour.

*   *   *

Lake wasn't hard to find. I only needed to make one turn and then I just followed the road the rest of the way until I saw a sign pointing down a smaller road appropriately named "Lake Village Road." Now was the real test: finding the HR building.

I once again grabbed the Sharpied map and used what deciphering skills I had to better understand it, but it was no use. There was nothing I immediately recognized around me that looked anything like something on the sketch of the Human Resources building. Annoyed, I continued driving straight until I could determine the next best step, ignoring any opportunity for a turn. I couldn't risk getting lost. Not now. Surely there would be more signs pointing me toward where I needed to be. There had been nothing *but* signs this entire time, including the one I just passed pointing me to the post office, which I didn't even know they had because it wasn't mentioned on the hand-drawn map.

As I drove, a collection of little canary yellow cabins appeared on my right, sequestered among generous clusters of pine trees. Behind the little neighborhood of houses were two matching buildings, one much larger than the other with its grand Colonial Revival architecture. That one had to be the Lake Yellowstone Hotel, where I expected I'd be working, with the smaller one being some motel-like version of it. All three locations butted up to a large, shared parking lot where a few lanes were blocked off by a velvet rope, which I assumed to be some kind of VIP parking.

I made one loop around the area, following the same two-lane road the entire time, and still couldn't find the HR building; from what I could tell, no signs pointed to it or identified it—it was either invisible or tucked away behind something larger and more obvious, like the general store. There was an office for the park rangers, a few dorms, a modest infirmary, and the lakeshore, but no Human Resources.

It took another two loops, a heated argument with the map, and a total of thirty minutes before I *finally* found it.

HR was a dingy little white trailer down a gravel path by the main entrance, blocked off by a sparse row of small boulders, meaning I wouldn't have been able to drive to it anyway.

There was no parking that I could see, so I chose a discreet lot belonging to a single-story employee dormitory nearby, which separated itself from the trailer by a thick wall of pines. In a frustrated huff, I grabbed my sweatshirt from the backseat and threw it on as I began walking over with a collection of check-in documents in hand, ignoring the extra bite in the air.

It was chillier than I expected it to be today, about fifteen degrees cooler than Missouri this time of year. Banks of snow remained glued to the base of every tree on the side of the gravel road, just as they were when I drove through the north entrance a couple of hours ago.

A lone bison was grazing a humble pasture just behind the dormitory I parked at, more than a couple hundred feet from where I stood. Thick, cottony clumps of fur dangled off his body, like fluffy caramel clouds in a deep chocolate sky. I could tell he was shedding his winter coat, something I hoped to do myself.

The Human Resources trailer was white and scraggly, faded and worn from years of baking under the sun at such a steep altitude. As I hustled toward the door, more and more desperate to escape the icy temperature, a laminated piece of paper fastened to the screen door caught my eye. Stepping up the rickety wooden stairs to get a better look at it, I read:

Lake Human Resources Hours:
8am–12pm,
2pm–6pm
Lunch Hours: 12pm–2pm

It was exactly twelve-thirty, a half hour into their lunch break.

I stood there, documents in hand, now looking at the sign instead of reading it, feeling confused and exasperated. I had done everything I was told to do—driven nearly twenty-four hours over the course of three days, waited in line for my ID and uniform, navigated my way around a national park without an internet signal, and found the impossible HR trailer using my wits and a sad excuse for a map. I'd spent hundreds of dollars in gas money, navigated rainy drives with one working headlight, come within twenty feet of a grizzly bear, and convinced myself to work a job in housekeeping for three months in one of the largest tourist destinations in the world.

These people *needed* to be here. I needed them here to welcome me in and tell me it was okay to rest now, to assure me I was in the right place and that my efforts had brought me to one of the most sacred places on Earth. But they weren't here to tell me those things I desperately needed to hear.

I pushed down the urge to hit something. I wanted to bang both fists on their flimsy wooden excuse for a door, snap it in half, and demand to be seen. I'd sacrificed my time, energy, money, and bandwidth to come to Yellowstone. If I'd received a better map and avoided that bear, maybe I might've made it in time. I could be unpacking clothes in my dorm room right now. I could be taking a hot shower and washing off the fatigue of a three-day car ride.

But I wasn't. I wasn't because Human Resources wanted to have a *two-hour* lunch break. That's how long it took me to drive from Gardiner to Lake. It doesn't take that long to eat a fucking sandwich.

Despite being cold, angry, and hungry, I knew my best option was to wait. In fact, it was my only option. I'd have to either stand around in forty-five-degree weather waiting for them or use up the remaining quarter tank of gas I had left to stay warm in the car.

Walking back to the car, now with rocks in my shoes from the gravel, past the bison, around the wall of pine, and onto the asphalt parking lot, I could only think of how angry and incapable I felt. It wasn't that a life-changing summer was out of the question, but more a question of the endurance it would take for me to see the value in waiting for one.

CHAPTER 4

---·· ✦ ✦ ✦ ··---

An hour and a half later, I was greeted by a thin, balding man named Kyle. He was dusting his hands off on his pants, attempting to clear crumbs of food from his slacks. Walking in, I felt the jolt of the screen door of the trailer slapping closed behind us as I allowed him to guide me to the back office.

It smelled like an old elementary school inside. Not exactly the worst thing, but it had that sort of unidentifiable odor that contains only the essence of smells, like when that one messy kid in class finally cleans out his desk before summer break after letting it all ferment inside for a year.

Inside the trailer I was greeted by manila folders and plastic eating utensils covering every inch of a row of kitchen counters. You could barely even see the laminate countertop. A cupboard mounted on the wall was slightly open, showing a small stack of paper plates. Across from the kitchen, by the screen door, was a dented metal desk displaying an old computer that reminded me of my elementary school's computer lab. Gobs of paperwork littered the keyboard despite no one being there. A battered couch rested against the wall right behind the desk near the back office we were walking into.

Another man was back there, resting easy in an office chair at another dented metal desk. He was the exact opposite of Kyle—round, bearded, and animated—and introduced himself to me as Mike. He didn't get up to shake my hand or anything. He just announced it from his mesh office chair behind his desk.

"Nice to meet you," I said in a quiet voice. My aggravation had cooled off since waiting for their office to reopen. By now, I was more concerned with doing whatever I needed to do in order to get up to my new room, unpack, and maybe get some food.

Kyle motioned for me to sit in one of the two empty metal folding chairs in front of his desk, which was positioned right next to Mike's. The three large window panels on the wall behind them looked out to the gravel path I'd followed here. I could just barely see the row of boulders at the top near the main road, paved with smooth, black asphalt.

Kyle eased into his chair with a sigh, sitting with a slight curve in his shoulder blades, like they couldn't straighten themselves back all the way. "Do you have your documents with you?" he asked in a dry, sandy voice. Actually, it reminded me of Napoleon Dynamite.

"Yes," I said, handing him the copies I got up north, confirming I received my uniform and work ID.

His heavy, bulbous eyes swam over the papers, loosely scanning signatures, dates, and document titles. He nodded to himself as he read before checking off some boxes on a clipboard on his desk. "Okay," he finally said, looking at me, "now, what kind of room do you want?"

For the first time since the drive in this morning, I felt confused. "What do you mean?"

"I mean, what kind of dorm do you wanna live in?"

His verbal alternation from *room* to *dorm* didn't exactly help; it was the same difference. I attempted to decode what it was he was trying to tell me but could only think to ask the next logical question: "What kind of dorms are there?"

Kyle answered my question with another equally confusing question. His protruding Adam's apple bobbed up and down inside his long, scruffy neck when he asked, "Do you party a lot?"

"Not really," I said, shaking my head.

"Are you quiet?"

"I guess."

Kyle broke his intent eye contact with me, which was beginning to make me feel self-conscious, to reach into his desk and pull out a singular paperclip. He held it up for me to see. "Are you *this* quiet?" he asked before dropping it onto the receding sea-green carpet. I couldn't even hear it hit the ground.

I stared at him, not entirely sure how to answer. "I, um…I don't know."

Just then, the screen door squeaked open and closed with a hard clap. Someone had walked in. We paused our conversation—if you could even call it that—long enough to eventually see a young girl about my age with long brown hair peek inside the open door frame, wearing a look of uncertainty. "Hi," she said with an uneasy smile. "Is this Human Resources?"

Kyle looked over my shoulder at her, poker-faced. "Are you one of the new people?" he asked in a monotone.

"Yeah."

"Have a seat."

She walked over and sat down in one of the empty chairs on my right, across from Mike, who hadn't really said much of anything except for a few interjectory *yeahs* and *by-the-ways*.

Kyle then turned to her and asked her the same question he asked me, temporarily ignoring the paperwork she had in hand. "Are you quiet?"

She shrugged, unsure of herself. "I guess so."

He reached down with a slight grunt to pick up the silver paperclip from the balding carpet and repeated his question once upright. "Are you this quiet?"

We watched the metal bit fall to the ground once more.

No one said anything. The girl blinked a couple of times and offered a chuckle, clearly feeling uncomfortable and at a loss for words. "Um..."

Kyle's wilted gaze swung back and forth between us, awaiting her response for only a few seconds before pulling out two bronze keys. "You guys are gonna be roommates," he announced. "I'm gonna put you two in the Pelican dorm, room 201. Don't worry; it's quiet."

Really, I thought.

"All the dorms are named after birds, don't ask me why—Pelican, Osprey, and Goldeneye. Osprey's got the parties and is right across the street from you. Goldeneye's farther behind you and for the older folks like us," he said, motioning to Mike.

Finally, after wrapping up the details and grabbing our keys, the new girl and I began the long walk back up the gravel path. Neither of us said anything for a minute. All I could think about was how amazing a shower sounded. I wanted to let the scalding hot water evaporate my fears and worries, my anxiety, and my stress. I wanted to scrub all the hours of driving off my skin and crawl into a warm, fluffy bed with my comforter up to my ears. I wanted to fall asleep wearing clean underwear. I wanted to—

"Hey, I'm Sarah."

Snapping out of my thoughts, I turned to see my new roommate looking at me with an easy smile on her face, far less forced than the one she had worn in the HR trailer. She had a perfectly straight set of teeth set in a strong jaw.

"Hi," I smiled back, "I'm Lauren." My dirty blonde hair sat in a tangled mess atop my head and the sweatshirt I was wearing had a stain on the front pocket.

"Where are you at?" she asked, referring to where I had parked my car.

I looked through the wall of trees on our left to the nearby parking lot directly on the other side of it. "I'm over there," I said, pointing to the white Acura you could just barely make out through all the pine needles.

"By that dark-looking building over there?" she asked, squinting.

"Yeah. I wasn't sure where to park because HR was such an awkward building to find. Not like you could drive to it anyway," I said, rolling my eyes and gesturing to the small row of boulders we were approaching.

"Right! Same here. I probably parked next to you then. I was hoping I wouldn't get a ticket since the sign said, *Employees Only*, but like, where else are you supposed to park, you know?"

"Exactly! It definitely wasn't easy to navigate. Actually, it took me probably half an hour just to *find* the trailer. Who knew it'd be a literal minute from the Lake entrance."

Two large elk stood grazing in a nearby pasture, their antlers bobbing up and down like buoys on a lake, as we continued making small talk until reaching our cars.

"I think we're supposed to go *there*," Sarah said, pointing to a small, one-lane asphalt entrance directly across the road. It curved behind another wall of trees where you could just barely make out a dark brown two-story building. "Next to the entrance it says *Employees Only*. Do you see that?" she asked.

"Yeah," I said, looking across the way at a dark wood sign with painted white letters on it that I could just barely make out. "Let's try it."

I followed Sarah across the main road onto the gravel path on the other side, opposite the one we walked up from the HR trailer. Large, rocky potholes flooded the employee entrance as we drove around the bend to see a wide parking lot in front of two long, rectangular dorms. A fair number of sedans and hatchbacks nestled comfortably into the lot, leaving enough options for me to choose a nice spot right in the middle of them all.

I got out of my car and walked over to the closest dorm, hoping to catch a building sign indicating it was Pelican. The two-story dorm, appropriately built like a log cabin, sat perpendicular to the wide parking lot with a thick, wooden staircase scaling up the shorter side. I read in white painted letters on its dark walnut sign, *Pelican*. Excited, I looked back to tell Sarah, who was already pulling a large duffel bag out of her forest green Chevy.

Across the lot was a matching dorm whose sign read, *Osprey*. I didn't plan on being there any time soon. For now, all I wanted was rest.

CHAPTER 5

Every morning over the next two weeks started the exact same way: I rolled out of bed, looked to see if Sarah had left for work, shuffled to the end of the room, scratched one side of my scalp, yawned while staring into my four-foot-long closet, put on the same uniform I worked in yesterday since only two pairs had to last me a week, threw my hair up, grabbed my jacket, tossed a book in my bag, and shoved in my earbuds. At the bottom of the stairs was a long strip of trees that paralleled the asphalt entrance toward the main road, where I would either see a couple of elk or a bison grazing on the west side of the dorm. I'd pass them by with a cautious eye, giving myself a distance of at least twenty-five yards as recommended by Mike at orientation, and dust up my shoes walking the long path to the hotel. There, I would clock in, listen to our half-hour morning meeting that could've easily been ten minutes, stretch with the housekeeping team in front of the hotel sunroom because I guess that's what team building looked like, work for ten hours, eat dinner, go home, shower, fall asleep, then wake up and start it again.

I did not like it here. That I was certain of.

I had no friends, did not enjoy my work, and operated in constant fear of doing something wrong, of living this experience incorrectly. I was supposed to be feeling grateful and carefree, to feel like I could *finally* be my own person, but I wasn't. Couldn't. I was no stranger to this feeling and often turned to it to enable my own punishment. It was a pattern of temporary discomfort, repeated attempts to remedy it, failure, resentment, and finally, self-sabotage.

I was always pretty reluctant to go out in college, but would occasionally do it because my roommate, who was also my closest friend, wanted to. We agreed one night to meet up at a nearby bar with some people who were more her friends than mine. I hadn't been to many bars or parties, in part because I was underage, but also because I thought both the music and social considerations sucked. If I was being honest with myself, I would admit that I went because I thought it'd be good for me.

I spent thirty minutes getting dressed up with her, applying mascara, concealer, a bit of blush, and wearing something casual yet classy—usually a flattering top with jeans. That part was always fun. The two of us left in her car and drove four minutes to Pine Street, a five-hundred-foot-long strip known for housing some popular bars, pubs, and restaurants. It wasn't anything to write home about, the town itself held just over twenty thousand people, but here I was with Frankie and a handful of other people I was about to meet, attempting to do what every college kid loves to do—*go out.*

Everyone was inside when we arrived.

"Hey, guys!" A girl with short blonde hair embraced my roommate in a big hug. She was wearing a red dress with a small slit up the side that complemented her figure well, and I found myself feeling jealous. I was wearing my last clean pair of jeans.

"Lauren, this is Kylie," said my roommate. I vaguely remembered seeing Kylie around and I thought we might've met once, but I played along anyway.

"Hi." I smiled.

"Hey! Everyone's over here. We were just hanging out," she said, motioning for us to follow her.

I was the last in line with Kylie leading the way, doing my best to push aside my nerves and mild jealousy. In the back of the bar were four people I'd never seen before, another girl and three guys. Kylie sat next to the girl and reached over to hold her hand, a beer in her other. She crossed her legs, the slit in her dress revealing the light skin of an athletic thigh.

I sat by my roommate since she was the only one I really knew and, for the next thirty minutes, I listened to everyone talk around me. People spoke about people, many of whom were lost on me, until a few members of our group got up to replenish their drinks, including my roomie.

Now alone, I began to feel even more antsy, especially since one of the guys came over to sit next to me. It was just one other person and us.

"So, you're Lauren, right?" he asked. He had a tall, wiry frame, a long face, and a tangly scruff that was just a little too long to be appealing.

"Yes. And you're...?"

"Thomas," he said, extending his hand to shake mine. "Sound tech major."

"Thomas," I repeated, shaking his hand. "Nice to meet you. I'm Lauren. Education." I nodded, referring to my own academic focus.

"Nice," he said, scooching in a bit closer to me. I couldn't tell whether he had done it to hear me better or just to be closer. "So how do you know Kylie?"

"Oh, I don't," I admitted. "At least, not as well as Frankie, my roommate. She's our mutual friend."

"Ah," he said before taking a sip of his beer.

"So sound tech. Do you like it?"

He shrugged, swallowing his drink. I couldn't help but notice the way his beard collected the excess from around his bottle's mouthpiece after he took a sip. "It's all right. I'm just doing it so I have a reason to be around more music. Do you like music?"

"Of course."

"What kind do you like?"

"All kinds," I answered, "but I'm mostly an old soul: Motown, classic rock, jazz, you know..." I noticed the way he was watching me, looking more interested than I thought was really necessary. His stare, still and soft, was beginning to bother me, and I subconsciously started to lean away as I spoke.

"What kind are you into?" I asked, hoping that would get him to talk more about himself so I could get his eyes off me.

"All kinds," he smiled, recycling my words. "Indie folk and underground stuff, mostly. Actually, I've got an album I think you might like if you ever wanted to come over and listen to it."

"It's not on Spotify?" I asked, clueless as to what he was implying.

He let out an awkward chuckle. "No, I mean, we could listen to it together at my apartment."

Uncomfortable now, I hesitated with my words. "O-oh, well, I—"

"We're baaaack!" Kylie exclaimed, returning to the group with Frankie and a couple of other people joining in behind her. Even though a part of me felt relieved to see them again, part of me felt frustration toward Frankie for leaving me alone with this guy. I didn't want to get with him; I just wanted to be around people and have good conversations, even though I didn't feel particularly connected to most of it.

Kylie was sitting with her girlfriend again, hand in hers. With the other, she pulled out a funny-looking object from her purse. "You guys, look what I brought—a kazoo!"

"What's that?" I asked.

She explained to the group, looking past me, "It's like this little horn you sort of hum into and it makes this sound like... well, I don't know, let me show you."

She began buzzing the tune of "Sweet Caroline" by Neil Diamond into one end of the contraption, which seemed more like a plastic harmonica with a blowhole on top. It came out sounding nasally and annoying, the way a large fly buzzing around your ear would.

"*Omigod*, you know who would love to see that?" Frankie asked before exclaiming the name of a person I'd never even heard of. Presumably another mutual friend.

At the sound of this person's name, everyone seemed to get up in a heap to go find them, supposedly believing they were here at the bar tonight, simultaneously leaving me to follow them around like the neglected member of the group that I was. Feeling lousier with every minute I spent with them, I got up and reluctantly began searching the dive with this tipsy cluster of people until we found whoever it was they were looking for, which didn't take long. In a matter of seconds, they began swarming this guy I vaguely recognized who was sitting on a bar stool.

I felt I was spending most of my evening playing catch-up. I could never just *be* with them the way they were all simply *being* together. When they moved, I followed. When I spoke, they barely looked at me. Being ignored felt like more of a companion than these guys were right now, until I eventually decided to just...leave. So, without notice and without a sound, I left.

I clearly didn't belong there—that felt true enough—and I didn't dare risk letting myself continue to be chipped away by people I would never even think to invite out for coffee. Why should I subject myself to hanging around them if my presence wasn't even respected? I didn't owe them anything.

So I left.

I walked one mile back to the dorms by myself, in the dark, at eleven-fifteen on a Friday night. In my heated state, I was more willing to risk being targeted on my walk home than I was staying another minute in that bar, feeling overlooked and excluded.

Thankfully, I made it back home but not without dried mascara streaks on my cheek. I took in a deep breath before daring to look at the texts on my phone that had been weighing down my purse halfway through my walk: *Why'd you leave???* *Where'd you go??*

Ignoring it, I could only manage to change into my pajamas and bury myself under the safety of my bed's warm covers.

Sometimes, I liked to pretend that this feeling was a needy, attached person who made it very difficult for me to see the benefits of being alone. She was a beautiful blue woman who liked to seduce me with intrusive thoughts of self-pity and inadequacy. Walking over to the hotel this morning, she whispered to me, *You traveled thirteen-hundred miles to feel the same way in a different place. What good is it to have big dreams if you don't have anyone to share them with? Why is it so hard for you to feel a connection with people?*

Sometimes, I thought of her as a friend. Even if she was sad and blue, at least she kept me company. We often shared our misery together, and if I got rid of her, who else would I talk to? It was stay with her or wait for another feeling to take her place, otherwise I'd be empty. And empty is bad. Empty means anything could happen.

The thing is, this sad, blue woman knows she can't hurt me. She knows there's this strange, invisible barrier around me that takes more effort than she can make to penetrate it. It is a feeling that I can only describe as *purpose*, but what that purpose was, I didn't know. I did know I could be a lot sadder if I didn't have so much purpose inside me. Sometimes I thought it would be easier to just let all the purpose go, but I know it wouldn't really, so I let them both co-exist, the sad, blue girl and my purpose, and most times, the paradox was difficult to navigate.

I had expected Yellowstone to change me. I thought all my biggest dreams and wishes were meant to be realized here. I had manifested this opportunity, hadn't I? I'd created it out of thin air for myself, hadn't I? But each day over the course of the week and a half I'd been here, when I'd go to work to scrub toilets and pick dried Ramen out of the carpet because the vacuums didn't work, it only reaffirmed my secret belief that Yellowstone wasn't meant for me.

Yet...I continued to believe.

I'd been working outside in the canary-yellow cabins and not the hotel where I had expected to be assigned. The hotel was warm and cozy with shades of maroon, cream, and mahogany and long open hallways decorated in white trim. Out here, we hauled mule carts of supplies behind us in the wind and rain to old, creaky cabins with confused, neutral color schemes and kitschy, fish-themed comforters. I'd get through two or three of them before making my way over to the employee dining room, or EDR, for lunch, which is where I was now. I didn't remember the six-minute walk over, but I found myself standing with a tray of food in my hand next to Sarah, who was asking, "Is it okay if we sit here?"

We were standing in front of a table with two girls I recognized from this morning's meeting in the hotel conference room. One had a perfectly disheveled messy bun and the other had a face that for some reason reminded me of a young Judy Garland. They looked up from their trays and gave us a brief look-over. "Yeah. Sure." Then the girl with the messy bun said, "Hey, you're new, aren't you?" She was talking to me. I had just taken a large gulp of water, so all I could do was nod. She said, "What do you think so far?" She didn't sound very enthusiastic.

I swallowed my water, feeling a slight pain passing through my throat from the volume. "I, uh—"

"It's ass, right?"

I couldn't help but let out a small laugh. "Yeah, a little."

"I'm Candice, by the way."

The girl next to her straightened up. "And I'm Piper. Don't worry; you'll get used to it. It's really just a matter of finding your rhythm. We've been here for about three weeks." She then turned her attention to Sarah, who was next to me. "What do you do?"

"Kitchen crew," she said with a lame nod. "Thinking about switching to the deli shop in the hotel, though. It's gotta be better than washing dishes all day."

She responded in a knowing kind of way. "I don't blame you. I've heard you guys sometimes have to get up at, like, five o'clock in the morning, right?"

Sarah smiled, showing her gleaming, straight teeth. "That's exactly why I'm switching."

After some small talk, it turned out that all three of them were part of this religious organization called ACMNP. It was an acronym for A Christian Ministry in the National Parks. I felt myself beginning to get a little nervous, fearing becoming an unwilling recruit, so I hunched over to focus on the small mound of wrinkly peas on my tray.

Piper said, "I'm actually supposed to give my testimony this Sunday! So that'll be exciting. I've been prepping for it most of the week."

Sarah beamed. "That's exciting! I hope it goes well. I'll probably be there this Sunday. Where's it at again?"

"The recreation room in the Lodge down the road. You'll see it; it's got an *Employees Only* sign on the door."

Candice then asked, "So are you in ACMNP?"

Looking up, I suddenly realized she was talking to me with the other two staring, awaiting my response. Self-conscious of my answer, I simply said, "No, I just came here to work."

"Well, if you don't mind me asking, are you religious at all?" she asked, pushing her thick, black-framed glasses up the bridge of her nose.

I shrugged, looking down at my peas again. "Not really. I guess you could say I'm more spiritual."

She nodded like she was satisfied with my answer. "That's a good way to be, just being open to different perspectives, you know? And don't worry; we're not gonna force you to join us or anything."

I felt the tension in my shoulders loosen and I found myself letting out a small breath. I didn't realize I'd been holding it.

"Yeah, it's pretty great," Piper added with a grin. "I don't know if Sarah told you, but we have a bunch of activities we'll be doing this summer that aren't church related at all, like white water rafting and hiking and stuff. So if you ever wanted to come or something, you'd be more than welcome."

"Sure, thanks." I nodded, with no intention of going to any of those things.

Our lunch break was almost over, so we got up to dump our trays and make our way outside. Sarah would just need to return to the kitchen, but the rest of us would walk over to one of the hotel's employee entrances, separate from the EDR, to clock in before returning to the cabins.

"So which dorm are you staying in?" Candice asked as we made our way across the large parking lot and down the hill toward the cabins.

"Pelican," I answered.

"Us too!" Piper chirped. "Which floor?"

"Second."

"Same here," said Candice. "Maybe we can all walk over to the EDR in the mornings for breakfast or something since we're all working together anyway."

I smiled. "That'd be great."

A small prickle of hope budded in my chest. I could feel my winter coat shedding.

CHAPTER 6

─────────··✦✦✦✦··─────────

It was the start of June and more people had begun to fill up the main floor of the hotel. Children carried iPads, parents carried travel documents, and tourists bore all kinds of straps, lenses, and gizmos draped around their necks and shoulders like graduation stoles. The number of guests in the sunroom, my favorite part of the hotel, had nearly doubled. While the outside remained its signature yellow with Colonial Revival accents, the inside was lovely and light; cream walls with flat, white beams that stretched across the ceiling. The sunroom jutted out from the walls of the hotel as a large bay window area facing the partially frozen Yellowstone Lake directly in front of it. Sarah and I started having coffee dates there. She had transitioned to the in-house deli, just down the hall and past the reception area, where we could get free shots of hazelnut syrup in our cups.

Our suitemates just moved in next door, too, where they're attached to us by the connecting bathroom. I forget their names, but one of them worked in the Employee Dining Room that Sarah had just moved from, and the other was going to be in housekeeping, like me. I'd seen her around the cabins in training for the past few days, so there was a fair chance she'd be placed out there with Candice, Piper, and me. Although I worked in the cabins I was mostly trained in Sandpiper, the two-floor motel-like building tightly tucked between the hotel and the cabins, which meant that, really, anything could happen.

The sky continued to be mostly gray and cold but sunshine occasionally broke through the clouds for a while. I learned to bring my jacket every day, too, mostly for the spontaneous afternoon rainstorms that I'd been conditioned to anticipate. Sometimes I wished I worked inside and didn't have to deal with these weather patterns that were weird to a girl from Missouri where it would now be in its last pleasant phase of late spring before turning hot and humid for the majority of summer. There hadn't been much rain there for the past year or two, so Wyoming's weather patterns were educational, if nothing else.

Working in the hotel and Sandpiper meant not having to deal with hauling your cart around in the rain or running to the main cabin office for a parka or checking for nearby bison and elk. You stayed inside where it was warm and calm and had a cart with four working wheels that you could push in front of you instead of two that you had to haul behind you like a mule. One room followed another in a logical, sequential order instead of a random pattern of cabin numbers that made no sense to the untrained eye.

I had been trained to put the lemon-scented bear-shaped soaps in the corner of the sink counter, replace the toilet paper roll when it was less than the width of my pinkie nail, and fill up the shampoo bottles in the shower when less than half empty. I was trained to put the dirty towels and pillowcases in the blue bag and the used bedsheets in the white bag, while keeping a separate white and blue bag for the clean and dirty washrags we used for the rooms, respectively. There were so many things we hadn't been trained for: how to interact with a fussy guest, what to do if we didn't have enough towels, what to say if the guests answered in their robes and slippers when you knocked on their door at eight in the morning. It took me three days and forty-five rooms to get it all right.

Today's big dilemma was running out of cleaning rags, or *blue rags* as we called them. They looked like they might've been white at one point, but something must've happened at the laundry facility up north because they now carried a faint blue stain on them, hence their name. Whenever we ran out, we were reduced to using one for the whole room while continuously nagging our linen truck drivers, or LTDs as we called them, to bring more by mid-afternoon before the guests started checking in, which usually didn't happen. This typically left me to ask a nearby room attendant for extras. In today's case, it was Candice, who'd been working in the cabins for the past three or four weeks. I asked if I could take a couple of hers in exchange for some extra coffee packets I had.

In the end, the new bundle of blue rags didn't come until we were restocking our bins of supplies at the end of the day. I snuck a handful of them to stick into my bin before they disappeared again and asked my inspector for the day to sign off my cleaning list I'd completed before heading up with a few other RAs to the hotel. There, we would ideally get the green light to clock out from one of our three managers.

I walked with the others up the massive hill from the cabin office and across the large parking lot behind the hotel, through one of the doors by the reception area. Up the two flights of stairs to the second floor and around the corner was the small housekeeping office that felt more like a large storage closet than anything. There, I waited with a small cluster of other room attendants for our turn to go into the back computer room Mary was in, hoping to not get assigned any more last-minute tasks.

The simple fact was nobody liked her. Mary was one of the two assistant managers in the hotel who I could only describe as a "corporate Marley": she had thick, ginger dreadlocks that were always swooped up into some kind of twist or bun atop her head, usually with a fake hibiscus flower clipped into it. She wore the same outfit every day, black slacks with a black blazer, and purple, smokey eye shadow with a thick helping of mascara. She was pretty with soft facial features, but it was her attitude nobody liked—borderline passive-aggressive. She was pushy in the nicest way, which seems almost impossible, and was a staunch rule-follower. The only way was by the books, and the clipboard she constantly carried was indicative of that.

When it was my turn, she called out from the room, "Come on in, Lauren!"

I waited for the person in front of me to squeeze out of the narrow door frame while I stepped out of the way to allow her by. At the end of every day as I stood in that room, waiting for them to let me go, I would look over at the two conference chairs in front of the gray metal desk and silently wish for them to ask me if I wanted to sit. I worked ten hours a day and only sat to take my lunch break halfway through the day. My feet throbbed incessantly for the two weeks before numbing themselves.

Mary looked up at me from the stack of papers in front of her, meeting my eyes with a false sense of warmth. "Hey there; how's it going?"

I smiled back out of politeness and shrugged. "Pretty good."

"Good, good," she nodded. "Got your room assignments for me?"

"Yes," I said, handing over the two-page list of room's I'd received at the beginning of the day, highlighted in nonsensical patterns of neon pink and yellow. Black checkmarks and sidenotes decorated the margins from all the rooms I'd attended, some of them which weren't even mine to begin with. Typically, once I finished my rooms, I'd be assigned to help another person who had fallen behind to help clean their rooms too. My inspector's signature was at the bottom, indicating that I had fulfilled my duties for the day. I cleaned fifteen rooms in total.

She studied it carefully, using a much nicer pen than the one sitting among the crust and debris in my uniform pocket to scan each row and note I made. "Looks good," she finally concluded with the same smile. "You can hang up your key and put the list in the tray outside the door. Thanks, girl."

I sighed a breath of relief as I turned around, hoping she didn't notice. No last-minute tasks. I was free.

"Oh, I almost forgot!"

A surge of dread flooded through me as I returned my attention to her. "Yes?"

"You can expect to receive a trainee within the next week or two. Things are starting to pick up around here and we're expecting a huge influx of new RAs in the coming weeks, so you'll most likely be doing more teaching than cleaning that first day." She nodded as she spoke, maintaining solid eye contact with me, assuming I was just as on board with this as she was. Even if I wasn't, it's not like I could refuse. After all, she was telling me, not asking me.

"No problem," I lied. I didn't know the first thing about training someone.

"And if you wouldn't mind, could you return that vacuum over there to the storage room next door and take that bag of recycling downstairs? Then you can clock out."

I nodded. "Okay."

Annoyed, I managed to finish at my most reasonable hour yet—a quarter to six. Would've been closer to five-thirty if I didn't have to do any of that other stuff. I've worked outside for as long as ten or eleven hours before, so tonight could've been worse. On the bright side, because it was before six, I still had time to stop by the dorms to change and get comfy before heading over to the EDR for dinner. Usually, I'd have to run over with everyone else before they closed at six-thirty, but if I was ever afforded the time to change out of my grubby, sweat-infused uniform before then, I'd take it.

Back at Pelican, I found Sarah water coloring on the floor, something she'd been doing a lot to pass the time. I said a quick hello and complimented her picture before hopping in the shower for a quick rinse. Sometimes if she was around when I got off, which wasn't as often as I liked, we'd grab dinner together. We thought it might be a nice gesture, though, if we invited our new suitemates to come with us. So, after hopping out of the shower, drying my hair, and throwing on some clothes, we crossed through the bathroom together to knock on their door on the other side.

"Hey, y'all!" she greeted with warmth. Her chocolate ringlets of hair barely touched her shoulders and freckles sprouted from her cheeks. This was my first time seeing her up close.

"Hey, Gretchen!" Sarah said, showing her wide smile. "Have you had dinner yet? Lauren and I are getting ready to head over to the EDR and were wondering if you wanted to come. Your roommate can, too, if she's around."

She beamed. "I'd love to come! No, she's not here, but I was actually starting to get super hungry and was about to head over, so I'm glad y'all asked me! I didn't want to walk over alone," she admitted.

Once there, I was disappointed to learn that tonight's grub was a subpar combination of grilled chicken with an olive-green bean side. For vegetarians, there was an option featuring Gardein chicken, which I took a small helping of. You could tell they were running out of ideas when they started mixing the vegetables together like that. Turning to our right, we grabbed helpings of salads and other more respectable, though repetitive, sides from the self-serve stand. We hopped up the short flight of five stairs to the main eating area to grab silverware and drinks before eventually spotting Candice, Piper, and a few other recognizable people in the middle of the cafeteria. Most of them were still in their work uniforms, others with damp hair and fresh sweatshirts, like me.

The three of us sat at the remaining seats at the end of the table, tuning into one of the inspectors talk about how he went hiking over at Canyon with some of the housekeeping managers. I learned his name was Dorian and he had dark, curly hair, like Gretchen. He was a bit shorter than some of the other guys at the table, but his voice was a smooth baritone pitch, making it very pleasant to listen to.

Piper spoke up next. "We were thinking of maybe going to Cascade Lake at some point with the group. I've heard that one's pretty good."

"With what group, the God Squad?" Dorian asked.

Piper rolled her eyes in clear annoyance, as if she'd had this conversation with him before. "It's *not* the God Squad; it's called A Christian Ministry in the National Park!"

He gave a short, dry laugh through his nose. "Okay."

"What hikes have you done so far, Dorian?" Candice asked through a mouthful of chicken while reaching up to adjust her messy blonde bun.

He was sitting across from her, leaning forward with his forearms crossed on the edge of the table, a crumpled napkin on top of his tray. "We've done Elephant Back, Storm Point, part of Mount Washburn..." he tallied aloud. "Actually, more of them are starting to open up now with the snow melting and all, so we're thinking of doing Fairy Falls up north at some point."

"Nice. Let me know how that goes. I've been wondering about it," she said, gesturing to the large chalkboard on the far wall next to us. In various colors of chalk, it acted as an announcement board advertising all kinds of employee-only activities: hiking groups, sports tournaments, meet-ups, and a couple of other items. Fairy Falls was scribbled at the top as the next group hike that would be happening in the next week.

I had no desire to hike Fairy Falls, despite the name sounding as magical as a scene from *Alice in Wonderland*. Instead, I sat there listening to everyone else talk about hiking, munching on my below-average, self-assembled salad. I abandoned most of the weird olive-green bean combo and half of my Gardein chicken after shunning its rubbery consistency, despite it being called "grilled." The chips I grabbed from a big serving bowl last minute were stale from being left out for most of the evening. Smothering it in guac helped a little, but not much.

"Are you a vegetarian?" I heard Piper ask.

Listening for a response, I heard none. I looked up and realized she was talking to me. "Am I a...? Oh, yeah, I am."

She leaned into the table and craned her neck to talk to me, cocking her head to the side, "How long have you been one?"

"Since about January maybe?" I answered before quickly adding, "But I'm not, like, up-your-butt about it, you know? It doesn't bother me if people eat hamburgers and stuff."

"What made you switch?" Candice asked. Turning to her, I suddenly saw more than just her eyes on me, waiting for an answer. Everyone was. I became uncomfortable with all this sudden attention.

"Well," I started, "at first, I did as an act against factory farming after seeing how badly they treated the animals and stuff, but now it's more for environmental reasons. Combats climate change."

She pushed her thick, black-framed glasses up the bridge of her nose, her expression unchanging. "Cool. You know Dorian used to be vegetarian, right?"

I looked at him, awaiting confirmation. He nodded with a shrug. "S'true."

"But not anymore?" I asked.

"Nah, stopped when I came here. No particular reason, really; just kind of started eating meat again."

"Gotcha." I gave a quick smile before turning back to my food. I found that openly identifying as vegetarian either prompted a—sometimes deep—discussion around ethics or judgment from heavier meat-eaters. Both of those things made me uncomfortable because I was the center of it—my choices were investigated and my mindset was examined, which were two things that felt a bit invasive to me. So, usually, I kept quiet about it.

Once it inched closer to six thirty, when the EDR began closing up shop, everyone started getting up one by one to dump their trays and down the remaining blue Gatorade in their plastic glasses. Some of the kitchen people began wheeling out soapy cleaning buckets on old service carts and slap their wet, blue-stained washcloths down on tables to wipe them down.

Suddenly, with no relation to watching dirty tables get cleaned, I got an idea.

CHAPTER 7

＊＊＊＊＊

"Hey," I said to Sarah and Gretchen as we walked down the external flight of metal stairs to the dusty ground below. The EDR was odd in that you had to climb up to it since the same kitchen that served us was attached to the hotel's dining room that also served the guests, which, for whatever reason, wasn't at ground level. "What if we went to Fishing Bridge and got milkshakes?"

Fishing Bridge was what you might call the next neighborhood over. It was three minutes away and had, supposedly, a diner inside the general store. I had heard a small cluster of people talking about it right after coming to Yellowstone. For the past couple of weeks, I'd been intrigued but not brave enough to go there by myself, and Sarah had been picking up more shifts lately. I thought tonight would be our best chance of all three of us going.

I also just really wanted a milkshake.

Their eyes lit up and after a quick glance at each other they agreed to go. "Yeah, sure," Sarah said. "Let's do it! I had no idea Fishing Bridge had milkshakes."

"Have you been there?" I asked.

"Nope."

"Me neither. Obviously." Gretchen chuckled.

We decided to head back to Pelican to grab our keys and wallets before taking my car a few minutes north to the general store. We walked up the rickety flight of wooden stairs to the second floor of the dorms, grabbed what we needed, then headed back down to the parking lot.

It felt a bit warmer tonight—not much, but a little. Summer was on its way. In the car, I cracked the two front windows enough to turn off the air in the car and let the wind pick up little blonde strands of my hair while driving down Grand Loop Road. Gretchen and Sarah talked while I focused on finding the sign for Fishing Bridge, which was hard to miss. I turned the corner and followed the two-lane asphalt strip toward the large, log cabin-like structure. The trees had duplicated themselves enough that you had to pay special attention to which part of the building you would need to park by. A conglomerate of various establishments all appeared one after another—a few random cabins, a car and RV repair center, a Sinclair gas station, the general store, and a visitor's center on the other side of the road.

To my surprise, the general store parking lot was fairly packed for a quarter to seven. A long, cream-colored sign greeted us in tall, vintage letters above stone columns: *Yellowstone General Store: Fishing Bridge*. Wooden rocking chairs with fake wicker seats decorated the narrow porch as we made our way through the double-door entrance, captivated by what was inside.

It was a comprehensive collection of all needs under the same roof; it was a gift shop, mini-mart, camping shop, and, yes, diner, which was way in the back, past all the merchandise and next to an inactive ice cream counter, probably because it struggled to get above sixty degrees and was still too early in the season.

In the back of the store were three elongated dining tables jutting out from the main serving counter up front, each with red, cushioned stools like a 1950s diner. It formed an odd, pixelated M-shape. We managed to secure three seats over on the far right among all the families and traveling couples.

It was only when we saw the menu that we realized milkshakes were six dollars each, and Sarah and Gretchen needed a little persuading that we shouldn't just order one and stick three straws in it. I don't know about Sarah, but Gretchen and I made about nine dollars an hour in housekeeping. We could pocket any tips that were left for us, but it was still early in the season and, consequently, there hadn't been many for us to collect. And, because we lived in a dorm, the cost of our rooms, utilities, the EDR, laundry services, and internet were automatically docked from our paychecks, even though the connection was nonexistent and we had only four washing machines for one hundred dorms. It was essentially college without the classes. Yellowstone on its own could be an expensive place to live—it took extra power, money, and resources to get basic supplies up here, like food, water, and electricity, so whatever we earned, we tried to keep.

Coming here with Gretchen and Sarah was exactly what I needed. I was starving to know anything about anyone. I thought of Humphrey Bogart in *Casablanca* when he grabbed Ingrid Bergman by the shoulders and demanded in that thick, mid-Atlantic accent of his, "Who are you really and what were you before? What did you do and what did you think?" That's what I wanted to do, grab anyone by the shoulders and demand that they tell me everything about them so I could experience something other than my own ruminations. I had felt alone for so long, internally as well as externally, and I wanted to get out of my head to pour into someone else's. That's one thing loneliness does to you: it forces you to reflect and learn lessons against your will that you can, one day, maybe use to help someone else.

I ordered chocolate, Sarah ordered vanilla, and Gretchen ordered huckleberry, something I quickly learned was an agricultural staple around here. Half the shop's merchandise was huckleberry themed. Sucking on her straw, trying to get the thick shake through the narrow passageway, Sarah said, "So are you in school?" It was a question I knew was for Gretchen since Sarah and I discovered early on that we were both majoring in elementary education.

The plastic top of Gretchen's Styrofoam cup was popped off and hanging over the side as she stirred the thick, indigo cream around with her straw, which was still stuck through it. "Psychology. Well, I'm actually double majoring because I can't pick between that and biology."

"That's so cool!" Sarah grinned. "I'm majoring in education. Actually, Lauren and I both are."

"No way! Like high school?"

Sarah and I looked at each other and giggled, "Definitely not. Elementary, like little kids. Big kids scare us."

I piped up. "Well, I actually think I'd want to work with older elementary kids, like fourth or fifth grade, but Sarah wants to hang out with the second and third graders."

Gretchen's face turned sentimental while scooping up some of her milkshake with her straw. "Aw, y'all, that's so nice! We need more teachers and you both are gonna be so good at it. I can tell."

"Thanks." I smiled on behalf of both Sarah and me. "By the way, I didn't ask, where are you from?"

"Mm!" Gretchen had just scooped a glob of milkshake in her mouth right when I asked that.

"Sorry," I said, "that was bad timing on my part."

She laughed through her nose, waving her hand in front of her as if to dismiss my apology. "No worries. I'm from Mississippi. Got a lot of family in the New Orleans area. Where are you guys from?"

"Missouri."

"Idaho," said Sarah. "Also, random question, are you in a sorority?"

Gretchen's attention was immediately caught. "Yeah, actually, I am. How'd you know?"

Sarah took another sip of her milkshake. It had softened significantly and climbed up through the straw without hesitation. "I don't know. I just had a feeling," she said, giving an awkward smile. "I hope you don't find that weird."

"Not at all! But yeah, I am," she said before naming a sorority I'd never heard of. "Are any of you?"

We shook our heads. "No."

Actually, I thought Sarah was when we first met at the HR office in that dingy little trailer. At the risk of stereotyping, she was much tanner than me with long brown hair, wearing Chacos and a long t-shirt that went just slightly past her athletic shorts. Her smile was bright white, and she seemed to embody the confidence I wished to have.

Gretchen had her chocolate ringlets looped through a scrunchie sitting on the top of her head, wearing a plain shirt under a cotton V-neck sweater and I was sporting a twelve-hour-old messy bun with a sweatshirt and jeans.

We were all so different in our own ways but shared one thing: we were natural. None of us had on makeup, name brands, or perfumes, apart from whatever smell the pine trees had rubbed off on us from working outside.

I wanted to say more about Gretchen being in a sorority, how I didn't expect it, but I lived in a constant state of fearing my own words. What if they were interpreted the wrong way? What if my questions weren't creative enough? Words always came more easily to me when I wrote them down instead of saying them out loud, so I tended to sit in that in-between state of dying to know more and not knowing how to reciprocate. I tried to think of more safe things to say to the two of them as I concentrated on drinking my chocolate shake.

"—Anyway, I think we should all go sometime," I heard Sarah say.

I pulled myself out of my thoughts and refocused my eyes on her from the menu I'd been staring at. "What? Sorry, I was still thinking about sororities."

She smiled. "No biggie, I just said I think we should try doing Dogshead Loop this summer. Some of the guys in ACMNP with me, Candice, and Piper were thinking about it and I wanted to see if you guys would be interested."

"I'd be down," Gretchen said. "Depends on the day, though. I'm off Sunday-Monday." She said it like it was one word: *Sundaymonday.*

"Me too; that's when I'm also off," I added.

Sarah perked up, suddenly excited by this idea. "Great! Let's plan on going after I leave the service on Sunday."

Through the many brochures I'd collected over the weeks, I knew that Dogshead Loop ran along the Lewis River Channel in the southernmost part of the park, just before you reached the exit. It was about eleven miles long. If I could walk about eight miles in an eight-hour workday, that meant it'd take us most of the day to get through.

I was beginning to know Sarah, Candice, and Piper well enough to assume that they most likely wouldn't try to loop me into anything I wasn't comfortable with, in terms of church activities or religious obligations. They just wanted to hike and so did I.

I'd been here for two weeks and hadn't seen much of the park.

It was about time I started.

CHAPTER 8

———————— ··•◆◆•·· ————————

It was in my last room of the day, and I was hand-picking small bits of Ramen Noodles out of the receding carpet of cabin 507 because the vacuum I got just moved stuff around. Not even the nozzle worked. Before that, in cabin 512, I had collected my best tip yet—two cents and a business card for a photography company somewhere out in Delaware. Whether that was intentional or accidental was hard to say, but either way, I'd have been happier if they'd left nothing.

Work had gradually started to wind down earlier and earlier. Half the attendants were in the cabin office restocking carts at the abnormally early hour of five o'clock. Once I'd picked out the remaining ramen, I could head over to do the same.

All three plastic bins in my mule cart were totally depleted— no more bedsheets, only two washcloths remaining, a measly collection of bear-shaped soaps, and four coffee packets, three of them decaf. I had used the last of my materials in this room, which wasn't even mine. It was assigned to another attendee who was overwhelmed with the number of rooms on his list, so my inspector for today gave me two of his, racking up a total of fourteen for me. That's what happened around here: as soon as they found out you were a fast worker, they'd punish you with more rooms.

I walked outside and chucked the handful of broken ramen into the open trash bag on my cart. I turned around, peeking inside the room for one final look over, before closing the door and locking it. The cart's weight had lightened significantly since this morning, so pulling it behind me across the street to the cabin office didn't take much effort if you didn't count the flat tire it was rolling on.

Parking it outside with the others, I started hauling the plastic bins inside, one by one, placing them on one of the few empty spots I could find on the floor. The first was for the bedsheets which, of course, were completely missing from the office's interior shelves. The linen truck drivers must not have come by today, meaning whoever got these bins tomorrow would have to restock them themselves. Annoyed, I threw on the plastic lid, clicking it shut, and moved on to the next: towels. There weren't many of those either, so I grabbed what I could before anyone else snatched them up and dropped them in. Amenities were last. I noticed a couple of rolls behind one of the other RAs nearby and asked them to grab them for me when Gretchen, who was a couple people down from me, called my name.

"Yeah?" asked, stacking the toilet paper rolls along one of the inside walls of the bin.

"You wanna grab dinner together after this?"

"Sure. Are you almost done?"

"Yeah, I just gotta grab a few more Tazos and then I gotta get signed off by Clyde." She was grabbing handfuls of orange packets of wild sweet orange tea packets from the shelf behind her.

Clyde, her inspector for the day, was sitting at this dinosaur computer in the back typing numbers into the system from his clipboard. I noticed the inspectors doing that every day while the rest of us restocked. I think it was a way to let the people at the front desk know what rooms had been cleaned and checked so they could start assigning guests to them. There'd been a few times when the inspectors had gotten chewed out by the receptionists because we could never finish on time. All rooms were meant to be cleaned no later than five p.m., but they never were because we were always understaffed. It was a vicious cycle.

"And after that," Gretchen added, "Tyler and I were thinking of going to Pelican Creek for a quick hike if you want to come. Nothing crazy; it'd be more of a walk. It's just past Fishing Bridge."

Tyler was one of the room attendants I sat with in orientation a while ago whom I occasionally saw wandering around with his cart in the cabins. Couldn't say I knew, or even *saw* him all that well. I only ever noticed his ginger hair because that was always the easiest thing to spot. I said, "Yeah, sure. That sounds good. You're just going straight to the EDR after this, then?"

"Yeah, that's what I was planning on doing. We can just walk up to management together and check out at the same time if that works for you."

"Yep, it does," I answered, throwing the last of whatever amenities I could find into my bin: soaps, coffee packets, tissue boxes, and plastic bags for the cabin ice buckets, even though no one really used them. The nearest ice machine was a quarter mile away in the hotel. Then, once Clyde pulled himself away from the computer to sign Gretchen's list and Dorian signed mine, we walked up the hill to the hotel to the second floor to return our keys and get clearance from Danica, the other assistant manager, with Mary, who must've been on her weekend today.

We were a few others in the housekeeping office, so we were able to just walk right into the open door in the back.

"Hey, guys!" Danica chimed, twirling around in her black swivel chair like it was a dress. She was the cutesy kind and looked a bit older than us, almost like a big, preppy sister who was friends with all the popular kids in school. The only difference was she shared a similar attitude to Mary in that she could also be "politely pushy."

"Hi," we simultaneously greeted back.

"Here are our lists," Gretchen said, handing hers over and prompting me to do the same.

Eyeing it as carefully as Mary had, she deemed them completed and handed them back to us. I took them and dropped them into the tray outside the doorframe with the others, crumpled and scribbled.

"You guys are good to go, but I'll need you to sort the recycling downstairs before clocking out," she said, returning to the sea of paperwork in front of her.

Gretchen and I glanced at each other. "I think Candice and Piper were doing that, weren't they?"

She looked up again. "Oh. Well, I'd still go downstairs just to check if they need help. Otherwise, you're free to go."

We turned around after agreeing, knowing full well they wouldn't need any help. They both worked so efficiently, especially Candice, that us going downstairs to help would be like adding two extra cooks to an already bustling kitchen. Besides, there wasn't much recycling to sort today anyway. Just in case, though, we walked down the stairs, down the hall, and through an unlabeled door, poking our heads into a garage-like room.

"Hey, do you guys need help?" I called to the pair, who only had one white trash bag left to sort through.

"No," they called back.

"Okay."

I shut the door and the two of us turned around, retracing our steps, past the reception area, stairs, and concierge desk, through another unmarked door approximately one hundred feet down the hall. Inside was a long, slanted, concrete hallway we'd walked through countless times to clock in and out by swiping our IDs through a computerized box next to which was a door leading to the back lot outside. Going this way allowed us a faster walk from the hotel to the EDR, even though our feet got increasingly dirtier walking across all the gravel. I could never escape that dusty feeling in my toes; it's like my shoes acted more as a membrane than a shield.

Inside the Employee Dining Room we met Tyler, who was dressed in regular human clothes, not a housekeeping uniform. It must've been his day off.

I followed Gretchen through the dinner line, up the five random steps, and into the main eating area, trays in hand. Tonight was much better—fried cod with mashed potatoes. The kitchen must've gotten a fresh shipment of food or something, or it might simply have been the start of the month.

"Hey," she said, plopping her tray down next to him at a half-filled cafeteria table, grabbing a seat.

He nodded in her direction. "Hey, what's up?"

"Nothin'. Just got off work and thought we'd grab a bite a bit early before heading out."

"Good plan."

"By the way, Lauren's gonna be coming with us if that's okay," Gretchen said before eating a piece of cod.

"To Pelican?" he asked, looking up and over at me.

"Yeah."

"Sounds good." He nodded as if my presence wouldn't have made much of a difference.

*   *   *

A modest trail greeted us off the earthen shoulder of the simple two-lane road about a mile east of Fishing Bridge. The two of them were talking about Greek life at their respective universities when we pulled into the modest parking lot. They kept saying something like "Hotty Toddy," though for the longest time I thought they were trying to say "hoity-toity." Of course, I had no idea what that meant and thought I was maybe mishearing things. I wasn't annoyed by the selectivity of this conversation, but I also didn't feel called to contribute. For the most part, I just kept to myself.

We strolled through the walls of pines split by the trail, like three hikers parting an emerald ocean. It looped around in a small circle and hit just below the mile mark. No hills either. Those same rounded lumps of snow decorated the bases of trunks and scattered rocks but were significantly smaller than when I first arrived back in May. It was still chilly, despite heading into the second week of June.

The heels of my feet still ached slightly from all the day's walking but had numbed significantly over the weeks. To distract myself, I returned most of my attention to my surroundings, particularly the sounds—Gretchen and Tyler's voices, the crunch of stray pebbles under my shoes, the wind sighing through the clusters of trees, a lone bird chirping somewhere off in the distance. I took a deep breath, filling my lungs with every smell I could, selfishly absorbing them all.

"So you're Lauren, right?" Tyler asked over his shoulder. I could hear the faint jingling of car keys in his pocket.

My eyes searched the air until they found his hazel ones in front of me. They complemented his ginger hair well. "Yeah."

"Where are you from, again?"

"Missouri. Just outside of Kansas City."

"Ah, a Midwesterner," he mulled in a calm, even voice. "You like it there?"

I shrugged. "It's all right, I guess. I think I'd like to move away at some point, though."

"Where to?"

Oh God, where *wouldn't* I want to go? I watched my feet move back and forth in front of me, sweeping in and out from under my hips with every step they took on the damp, gravel path. "I don't know," I pondered aloud, "maybe Oregon or Colorado or something." Maybe it was basic of me to say that—every young adult wanted to end up in Colorado. "I think I'd even like to live abroad for a while."

Something in his voice changed. "Really?" he said, more as a statement than a question. "Where would you want to live?"

"England or Amsterdam, maybe. I wouldn't have a language barrier in England and I've heard Amsterdam can be pretty affordable. There'd be a bunch of other countries nearby that I could travel to over the weekend, too, if I wanted."

"Nice," he said, raising his eyebrows, then he went quiet. I worried if I'd maybe said something wrong, if I showed off too much or something. I wasn't trying to. I was just telling the truth.

"Would you want to live abroad?" I finally asked, thinking maybe it was my lack of reciprocity.

He let out a brief laugh. "No, probably not. I like where I am."

"Where's that?"

"Georgia."

"Do you like it there?"

"It's all right," he shrugged. "Good music. Not too far from Nashville."

"What kind of music do you like?"

"The usual, but also alternative stuff."

Gretchen suddenly whipped around to look at me. "Dude, you *have* to listen to Rainbow Kitten Surprise. They're so good; you'd totally like them."

Tyler piped up more than I'd seen him in the past six minutes, "Hey, did you see them in Nashville last year?"

"Yes!" she exclaimed, "Oh my God, they were so good. I thought 'Goodnight Chicago' sounded amazing live! By the way, Lauren, not to be a creep or anything, but you have really good taste in music. I'll hear your phone playing stuff when you're in the shower and it's honestly so similar to mine," she laughed, flush with embarrassment.

I smiled a modest thank-you.

If there was one thing I was proud of, it was my taste in music. That was my parents' doing; anytime we cleaned the house, drove in the car, worked in the yard, or even camped, there would be music. I learned to appreciate rock, jazz, Motown, classical, and contemporary tunes. I was an old soul at heart, and it often took twice as much effort to enjoy the "Best Top 40" or the more indie stuff, like Rainbow Kitten Surprise.

We soon came to a shallow string of trees on the side of the trail that hinted at a beautiful beach. Cutting through it all together to get a better view, I could feel the temperature cooling as we slumped down the sandy hill. The breeze from the shore lurked around my ankles like pools of invisible water. While I followed them down the bank, derailing from the walking path, I swung my drawstring bag around that I'd been carrying and pulled it open to retrieve my dad's old Canon camera.

"Whoa," Gretchen said, noticing it when we got down there. "What's that?"

I held it up for her to see. Most of it was black with a dash of silver across the top where all the controls were. "It's a Canon AE-1," I answered, sounding out the label on the front. "My dad gave it to me before I left."

She walked over to get a closer look with Tyler trailing behind her and I explained how it ran on film and what to do if they wanted to take a picture. "The lens doesn't zoom; it only focuses. So if you want to get a close-up of anything, you have to physically move to the position you want. Then you twist the lens until it focuses, like this. After that, you click the little button up here and move this black lever back to shift to the next frame. And that's basically it."

I let each of them take a couple of shots. When they tried to give it back, I assured them they could take more if they wanted. I had plenty of film, but they declined. It was mine, they said, and I should be the one to use up the film.

For a long while we walked and talked around the shore, snapping pictures and dragging sticks along the wet sand, drawing out letters and smiley faces in the sticky, copper sand.

At one point, Gretchen put her phone on a large nearby log on self-timer.

"Guys, c'mere!" she said.

Tyler and I looked up from our sand doodles and took note of what she was doing. We scrambled over to where she was and posed with all three of us wrapping our arms around each other in a short little line, shoulder-to-shoulder.

The camera, I guess, was set to take multiple pictures in a row, though Tyler didn't know that. He escaped our embrace only to realize it was still clicking, so he started galloping toward the camera, arms open wide like he was chasing it, while Gretchen and I stood there laughing in the background.

When it began to get cooler and darker, we decided to head back. As we meandered back through the woods and back to Tyler's Subaru, he invited us to come over to his room later for a showing of *The Office*. I've heard them having watch parties down the hall in Pelican for a while now. They would roar with laughter and scream at the cringey office behavior, which is what the entirety of the show was based on. I knew all the parts they were laughing at, too, because I'd seen it twice.

"The usual group will be there," he said as we tottered back up the sandy hill and back onto the earthen trail. Though what "the usual group" was, I had no idea. This was the first time I'd been invited.

"If either of y'all aren't doing anything, you should come over."

We agreed without hesitation. Nothing sounded better to me than lounging around with a bunch of co-workers, eating vending machine snacks, wrapped up in a warm blanket. And the best part was, I knew no one would be trying to impress anyone because we were all here for the same reason: to be a part of something, to *feel* something beyond our daily lives. I could go home and watch *The Office* a thousand miles away back in my own room if I wanted to, but it wouldn't carry the same meaning as lounging in a crowded dorm room with budding new friendships because I'd be missing that essential connection with other people.

That's all I wanted. I didn't want love, I didn't want romance, I didn't want the chase.

I just wanted friends.

CHAPTER 9

--- ··◆◆◆·· ---

Tomorrow was Sunday, and Sarah and I had confirmed with the ACMNP group that we'd be hiking Dogshead Loop then. We thought it'd be a good idea to get any helpful second opinions before starting, so we decided to speak with a ranger about any potential hazards we'd need to be aware of. A brochure could tell you only so much. Plus, we needed to get a permit and register for a campsite along the trail since we wanted to camp overnight to break up the eleven-mile hike.

We walked into the Fishing Bridge Ranger Station just up the road and found an older man sporting a forest green uniform with a nametag spelling out "Frank" in bold, capital letters. He had a fair number of leathery wrinkles on his forehead and looked like a no-nonsense type of guy.

Sarah and I looked at each other, silently deciding who should be the first to break the silence. Ultimately, she was the one to initiate. "Hi." She smiled with that lovely charm of hers. "We're looking at maybe getting a permit and registering for a campsite somewhere along the Dogshead Loop trail, please."

He took a long breath in. "Weeeell," he finally said in a dark, raspy voice, drawing out the vowel as he exhaled, "that trail's still got a decent amount of snow and you're more likely to encounter bears in the backcountry."

His response caught me off guard. In a weird way, I was a little taken aback by Frank's lack of, shall we say, *spirit* for helping two young women navigate the park. I guess I shouldn't have been, though, since he didn't even greet us when we came in the door. He only glanced in our direction before returning his attention back to whatever he was doing behind the reception desk.

"Right, but we heard it was open. We've also got bear bags and stuff," Sarah answered.

Did he just roll his eyes at us? I may have imagined it; it happened a little too quick to say.

"It is open, and it's gonna take more than a bear bag to stay safe in the backcountry. You're gonna need bear spray for each of you and those can be expensive," he said.

"We've got two," I replied before Sarah could speak, feeling my cheeks beginning to heat up. *He's not trying to discourage the two of us from hiking, is he?* "Employees get it for forty percent off at the general store and we got ours upon arrival."

He failed to acknowledge my response. "If you take this trail, you're also going to be crossing through a pretty good stream of water. 'Bout three feet deep with a current."

"We know how to cross streams—you unbuckle all the latches of your pack before crossing so it doesn't weigh you down if you get swept underwater," I countered. If Sarah didn't know that before, she did now. Dad told me about that trick on the way up to Yellowstone no more than a month ago.

He gave us a hard look, his expression stiffer than before. "You got anyone else comin' with you?"

"Yes, three other people," Sarah said. "One other girl and two guys."

Frank seemed to be considering this, making silent judgments in his head. Without speaking, he pulled out what looked like a planner and began listing off the available campsites. "There's one at the halfway point after you cross the river. It'll have a little stake in the ground with the number on it." Then he slipped us a piece of paper with the camp information on it and a permit to fill out. "You're going to stick this on the dash of your car right up by the window. Either of you have a reliable car?"

"Yes, I do." I spoke a little louder this time.

"What kind?"

"An Acura TSX." I wanted to punch the misogyny right out of this guy's mouth. I wanted to see it dripping down his wrinkly little chin in the form of an apology for making this such an unnecessarily difficult process for us. Because he was a ranger, though, I didn't want to risk getting myself into any trouble. I was afraid to make any kind of scene out of fear he'd call for backup or hold me in contempt of court or something. He had a whole squad inside that walkie-talkie on his desk and I had nothing.

Frank gave me a look after I told him what kind of car I had. It was judgment.

"That'll be twelve bucks."

After forking over a small wad of cash, we were told we'd need to watch a thirty-minute bear safety video before leaving. Sarah and I sat in chairs in the far corner across from his desk like a couple of school kids in trouble. What I really wanted to do was grab him by his uniform collar and whisper into his raisin of a face, "I work outside, Frank. I know there are bears." There's also bison and elk and moose and mosquitoes and poisonous berries and raging rapids and infectious diseases, but you know what? We're going anyway. Because that's what you *do* in Yellowstone, Frank. You go outside.

*   *   *

It was seven a.m. when my phone alarm sounded the next morning. I took a good minute to stretch under the warm weight of my covers, then turned my head toward Sarah from the other side of the room.

I whispered, "Hey."

Her head turned. "What?" she whispered back.

"You wanna have an adventure today?" I smiled.

We'd both been in a state of high anticipation for the last twenty-four hours. Hiking, new sights, breaking in our hiking packs. I hadn't been able to try out any of my camping equipment yet, like my mini stove-top burner and matching pot, and I was excited to later today.

"We should probably stop by the gennie for some extra supplies," I said, wiping the sleep from my eyes.

The *gennie* is what some of us had been calling the general store. Any store was a gennie, didn't matter where it was. However, I was referring to the one just around the corner from the hotel, a quick drive away from us.

Sarah nodded. "Good idea."

The plan was to spend the morning prepping our overnight packs leaving time to get some snacks, ramen noodle cups for dinner, extra sunscreen, and some extra water to go with our Nalgenes, just in case. We'd be meeting up with everyone else around eleven or so before driving an hour south to Lewis Lake, so we had a couple of hours to get ready.

At the gennie, Sarah was convinced we'd need to bring more than just a few extra water bottles in case there weren't any other water sources nearby besides the stream—we needed a *gallon* of water.

"What about our filters?" I asked. "I've got a little UV light water bottle filter we could use." In preparation for Yellowstone, I'd researched all the different kinds of water filters—there's iodine treatment, pumps, UV, squeeze filters, and of course, boiling. I bought a UV filter because I'd heard it was more effective at clearing toxins, and it came as a little orange water bottle, about twenty-four ounces. I began to wonder, though, if that would be enough. Plus, we didn't know how far away the campsite would be from the Lewis River Channel.

Frank said the campsite was just beyond a stream, but never specified exactly how far. A half mile? One? Two? I did acknowledge that buying a literal gallon of water to carry around in our packs would be overkill, but the other part of me thought, *What if? On the off-chance we got lost or underestimated our resources, it might be better to over-prepare than under-prepare.* So, after getting what I needed, I watched Sarah buy a gallon jug of water at the check-out station.

Back in the room, she shoved it down into the base of her backpack, assuring me she would be the one to carry it since it was her idea. "Plus, we can use it for cooking tonight if there's five of us that are going to be eating anyway. You've got stove supplies, right?"

"Yep. I've got a couple packs of ramen and some protein bars, so I think I should be good for tonight and tomorrow morning. You got the topographic, right?"

"Yep." She held it up in the air and waved it around for me to see, like a lottery ticket.

Topographic maps, I remembered my Dad explain, were essential. They were more useful than regular maps because they showed the elevation of every area in Yellowstone. That way, you didn't under- or overestimate the terrain when you planned a hike. Eleven miles on a landscape map was different than eleven miles on a topographic because the landscape map didn't take into account all the winding and climbing you'd be doing over the hills and around the trees. It was non-linear.

Eleven fifteen came around and we were ready to roll, just fashionably late for our backcountry escapade. We shoved as many packs as we could into the trunk of my car, which we could just barely shut. Then we got the three people in the back seat to hold the excess.

This was going to be my first-ever overnight hike. I felt nervous, anxious, excited, proud, and wonderful, as if it was the first day of school and I was getting to meet my teacher for the first time. I'd get to use all my new supplies, fresh from the store, and explore my new surroundings.

I was grateful to be in front of the wheel because it gave me something to focus on, something to direct all my energy toward. It was an easy drive, too, about forty minutes or so. All I had to do was follow Grand Loop Road south, past the West Thumb Geysers and the Continental Divide, down to Lewis Lake where there'd be a sign off the side of the road pointing to the trailhead. Sarah rode shotgun with the map and hiking brochure in hand to make sure we were going in the right direction.

It was in the upper sixties, one of the first warmer days we'd had. The sun was shining, and I had a good feeling in my heart, so I cracked the two front windows. All the roads in Yellowstone looked the same: a two-lane highway that capped at forty-five miles an hour with nothing but pine for miles on either side of the road. It was like the road was merely a crack in the park, a simple scratch among the millions of acres of wildlife, hot springs, meadows, prairies, wildflowers, and mountains. With every drive I took, I was swallowed up by the perfumes of pines, thick and musky with a citrus undertone. I carried it on my clothes and in my hair.

When we arrived at the trailhead, buried under a canopy of conifers at the end of the narrow entrance, we were the only ones there. No other cars were parked in the faded asphalt lot. I remembered to stick the permit on the dashboard while everyone scrambled out to uncramp their legs and grab their packs from the trunk.

The trail was quiet with shade and old, dusty footprints. I was reminded of an old walking path my dad and I used to take in the neighborhood across the street from us. The path sat low to the ground while the houses all were higher up on the hills, offering a good distance between us and the sounds of neighbors. We would wind through trees and over bridges and take detours to the rocky creek that flowed just beyond the honeysuckle bushes. I loved that walking path.

My eyes followed the trail all the way down until I noticed a slight bend in the path where it transitioned to a rocky terrain of charred trees and dried-up hills. As I walked closer to it, while Gretchen and the rest of the group talked, I concentrated on uncovering more of the landscape. It was blackened and barren, implying a forest fire at some point in the past, but how far in the past was difficult to say. One of the more interesting facts I'd learned since living here was that not all forest fires were bad. In fact, some trees needed fire to grow—many of those pinecones contained a wax coating that was so thick it needed to burn off in order to regenerate. They needed to be cracked open to let the life in.

Both guys in the group, thin and wiry, took the lead with Sarah in the middle, her brown hair coiled into another charming braid, Gretchen next with her ringlets bouncing around her shoulders, then me. This seemed to be a pattern, me being in the back, but most times I didn't mind it. It always gave me a chance to think or, depending on who was with me, have a deeper conversation with them, though until now there usually hadn't been many people to walk with.

Walking always soothed me, but I had never been able to figure out why. Maybe it was the steady rhythm of my feet hitting the ground or the way the sounds of nature just seemed to shower down all around me like spring rain. I don't know, but I do know it allowed me to *be*—to simply take my space in this world and for that to be enough.

The flat ground beneath us soon changed to a gradual incline as we made our way through the barren pine trunks and charred rocks. My legs, strong and lean, pushed against the ground, quads and calves constricting and releasing in a steady pattern—left, right, left, right. My thoughts would continue to drift in one ear and out the other, and I would temporarily find myself forgetting that I was even walking or breathing in the first place.

Four miles later, we reached a quaint little creek deep in a forested part of the hike where we could see just a brief glimpse of the Shoshone Lake through the dwindling wall of pine. It took up the entire horizon, saturated in a dark shade of teal. The slight breeze in the air had picked up a bit of the water, offering a nice cool brush of wind against our dampened foreheads.

"Hey, guys," someone called out, "let's take a break here."

Nobody argued.

Everyone threw their packs down on the ground, unclicking their belts and unzipping their bag's pockets to grab their water bottles. I wish I could say mine tasted cool and refreshing, but it didn't. It was pretty lukewarm and rather underwhelming, mostly because my plastic Nalgene wasn't insulated and had been baking under the warm sun for the better part of two hours. Luckily, it was a little more than half full.

I turned to Sarah, who was sitting on a nearby log with her monster pack between her legs. "How ya holdin' up?" I asked, referring to the giant gallon of water she'd been lugging around since starting.

She shrugged, something she didn't often do, and attempted a loose smile. "Eh. I'm managing."

"Want me to carry it?"

"No, I got it. We're getting closer to the campsite anyway. Actually..." she trailed off, scanning our stopping point.

Reading her mind, I looked around and noticed all the small clusters of campgrounds surrounding us, each with a brown-coded post staked into the ground next to each one. It didn't seem like we had made it to the halfway point, but we decided to look around for ours anyway. We searched for a few minutes, bending down and eyeing all the nearby posts for "8S1", but no luck. Figuring it'd be just down the trail a bit farther, we decided to have lunch now rather than later. After all, it'd be our only opportunity until we found our campsite.

When it came to hiking, it was important to keep in mind how risky it was to take a break that was longer than necessary. If you took a break for too long, you risked losing your momentum and that wasn't good. Your legs became tired, your body relaxed, and you limited your trail experience by prematurely ending your hike. It was similar to getting up in the middle of the night to use the bathroom quickly enough so you wouldn't "lose" your fatigue. This was the opposite of that: taking a break short enough to do what you needed to do without compromising momentum.

Within the forest was a small creek we'd need to cross before making it to the Shoshone Lake beach on the other side. That is, it looked small from where we were. Up close it was pretty active, with small rapids and bubbles of water rushing through the wide canal—likely all the melted snow that had come from the nearby mountains. Everyone seemed to have a good amount of drinking water left (not to mention the gallon jug we brought).

Packing up our bags and looking around for any other alternatives, we deduced there would be no way around it and we'd have to go through it—well, technically *over* it. The thick trunk of a conifer appeared to be lying across the top of the creek in the form of a makeshift bridge.

We each walked along the length of the tree, arms outstretched like human airplanes, trying our best to remain balanced, especially with heavy overnight packs on. As I hobbled across it, I glanced down at the water. It was difficult to say how deep it was, and frankly, I didn't want to find out.

I concentrated on putting one booted foot in front of the other, feeling the bumps and curves of the rough bark through my soles. The rush of the water beneath me stirred up a chilly draft, inviting goosebumps to sprout up all over my arms. Ignoring just how cold I'd suddenly become, I maintained eye contact with the remaining three feet in front of me.

Right…left…right…left…

Reaching the end of the trunk, I gauged the optimal point for jumping off—about one foot out from the base. I'd just need to be careful of some of the roots sticking out from the bottom of the tree.

3…2…1!

I landed in the open spot amongst some little branches and twigs, exactly where I'd intended to, with minimal scratches. Then I hastened out of the way to make room for Gretchen, who was behind me and would be making the same jump.

Relieved to have successfully crossed the busy stream, we traveled through the last of the forest where the thick pines immediately gave way to a vast horizon of teal blue waters— Shoshone Lake. Beyond the thick forest was a warm field of native grasses that led to a thin, rocky shore of rounded, silver pebbles. I saw calm rolls of white waves lap up against the edge of the rocks the same way hammocks swung back and forth in the breeze. A few stray canoes and kayaks in various bright colors lined the shore, indicating water-bound tourists taking a break nearby.

Seeing this view was like seeing a white flag or a finish line. It seemed to call out to us, "Hey, you've made it! Somewhere around here is your camping spot! Come relax by my waters and enjoy yourselves now!"

According to the directions Frank gave us, though, we still had another mile or two to go. He mentioned something about crossing a stream or a river and we hadn't done that yet. It had to be around here somewhere.

"Hey, Sarah," I said, looking around for her. "Do you have that map still?"

"Yeah," she said, turning around. "It's in my front pocket just under that meshy covering there."

I tugged it out from under the purple netting stretched over her pack. "I wanna make sure we're still heading in the right direction. Frank mentioned crossing that stream, remember? It just seems a little weird how we'd have to cross water to get to our camp spot. It seems like the hike ends here."

When the others saw Sarah and I huddled around the map, they came over to take a look at it too. Five different index fingers traced along every crevice of southern Yellowstone, reciting Frank's directions while doing so.

"I think we're supposed to go this way," one of the guys said.

"No, that takes you on a whole different trail. See?" the other one reasoned, pointing to a fork in the path.

Gretchen piped up. "Maybe you're holding the map wrong."

"No, it's supposed to look like this," Sarah said.

We stood huddled like this for nearly ten minutes, trying to remember Frank's directions. *Follow this bend in the path, take this turn here, cross the little river channel there, and you'll come to a campsite that says* 8S1. We couldn't locate the campsite on either map, the topographic or the zoomed-in version on the brochure. We didn't pass it anywhere along the trail or anywhere else nearby. In the end, though, we decided to cross the stream, as Frank said to. He was the ranger.

Before crossing, we paused to change from boots to sandals. Mine didn't have the best gripping on the sole, but they were all I had. Wearing boots underwater could weigh me down and they might shrink when I left them out to dry. The only reason I knew the latter was because in my high school cross country practices it wouldn't be uncommon to run in the rain, so to combat any shrinking, we'd have to stuff our shoes with newspapers to retain both the shape and size.

Nervous, we made our way into the water, one right after the other, like little ducklings crossing a road. It was just as busy as the creek's stream, but on a much larger scale. The initial cold shocked my feet as I stepped in, reminding me of the freezing ice baths I'd take with my high school running team before race days. It was the kind that shocked you and made your muscles lock up. Supposedly, it flushed all the lactic acids out of your legs to optimize your performance, but each movement, no matter how minor, would punish you with frigid, aching pains all over your body.

I had no choice but to keep moving. First my feet, then my ankles, followed by my shins and knees. It didn't take long for the tide to reach my waist, clutching it with its arctic fingers. Its strong grip pulled me downstream, but I refused to give. Against the frigid tides, I kept my core strong and my feet attentive to the ground. Once again, I felt every bump, dip, and curve through the soles of my sandals, praying I wouldn't roll my ankle against a sudden drop in the floor. It consumed all my attention.

Everyone's packs were unbuttoned, including my own, so the weight I originally carried on my hips immediately transferred to my shoulders. This made hauling the weight more difficult, but if I slipped and got carried away, I'd at least be able to escape it fairly readily.

Every few steps or so, I would check in with Gretchen, who was behind me, by shouting over the roaring current, "Doing okay?"

And every time, she would shout back, "Yeah!"

When we made it safely to the other side, climbing onto the gravel floor on our hands and knees, against the jagged pain and scratches, we lay on the ground like wet laundry. Everyone was drenched from hip to toe. Our legs were beet red and coated with goosebumps, numb to whatever warmth the sun provided. Relief washed over me, soothing my nerves and slowing my heart rate to a normal, steady beat.

The worst was over.

"Are you guys okay?" Sarah asked.

A mix of affirmations met her question, some people giving a thumbs up and others muttering something along the lines of, "We're good."

"That was intense," one of the guys said.

"No kidding," answered Gretchen.

"So where do we go now?" the other guy asked.

We all looked directly behind us to see a massive hill that looked more like a rounded cliff. Miscellaneous roots curled out from the dry, cracking soil. The only way forward was up.

Dread vaguely manifested itself somewhere in my stomach, though I was too cold to tell where. My goosebumps hadn't yet disappeared either. They'd been just as prominent as when I emerged from the water five minutes ago. I hadn't realized how cold I still was.

We rested a few more minutes, mustering up our remaining strength to scour the giant, ten-foot climb in front of us. The guys went first, using the roots as stairs and ropes to hoist themselves up and over the dusty mound, then the remaining ladies, mimicking their movements. My legs felt like noodles and my arms weren't any better. Every muscle contraction felt like a chore.

We spent the remainder of our hike looking for the infamous *8S1* campsite. We walked for roughly a mile and still didn't see it. Thinking we might've underestimated its proximity, we hiked another mile. Then another. Still, we didn't see it anywhere. Not even *one*. We referenced Sarah's map more times than I could count, retracing our steps and re-rationalizing our decisions.

"Dammit, Frank…" I kept hearing myself sigh.

Sarah shook her head back and forth in defeat. "He must've given us the wrong directions."

"Or shitty directions," Gretchen corrected.

Sarah raised her hands on top of her brunette head, the way runners do at the end of a long race. "Why don't we just pick an open spot somewhere off the trail? I've been lugging this gallon of water around for eight miles. I feel like I'm in basic training."

The guys agreed. "Yeah, that's a good idea. There was a spot I saw a little ways back that might be good," the leader of the hike said.

What we were doing was illegal. You were never supposed to camp off the side of the trail because, if something happened, the rangers would have a harder time locating you. I didn't feel good about it, but it was our only option. We couldn't keep walking like this; we were too far away— and too exhausted for that matter—to repeat our trek back to the campsites we'd passed before on the other side of the river channel.

There was an open, circular area within the cluster of trees we'd walked into. It opened up just wide enough to fit all of our tents in there with room to set up our hammocks off to the side. I offered to take everyone's supplies—toothpaste, extra snacks, deodorant, anything with a smell—and hang it up in a bear bag, with Sarah's help.

It was a white, meshy laundry bag that scrunched up at the top. We looped some thick, white rope through the bag, then tied either end around two large rocks. Then we chucked each rock over a tall branch from either tree and pulled them down to the ground, elevating the bear bag. It essentially acted as a pulley system. You wanted to keep it at least two hundred feet away and roughly fifteen feet off the ground by hanging it between two trees in mid-air. The goal was to lure any potential bears away from our campsite—if they smelled food, they smelled us. Although bears were a likely possibility when you traveled in the backcountry like this, I didn't expect to see any, nor was I all that worried, probably because of my lack of energy. The bear bag was hung, I had my bottle of bear spray nearby, and that's what was important.

Now that we'd set up camp, everyone ambled off to their own sections of the woods, most of them retreating to their tents or hammocks. I went back into the tent Sarah and I would be sharing to change out of my wet clothes and into slightly warmer ones before retiring to my hammock to take a mid-afternoon nap like everyone else. When I emerged from the tent, I was sporting an awkward combination of socks, sandals, a black thermal shirt, blue swim shorts that I thought were hiking shorts when I originally bought them, and a simple baseball hat to keep the mosquitoes away.

Mosquitoes were the biggest problem in Yellowstone—probably more than bears, in my opinion. So before rolling into my hammock, I coated myself generously in bug spray. The smell was awful; it had that sharp, sour odor that came from its miscellaneous mixture of chemicals, but it worked well enough for me to fall into a relaxing, undisturbed sleep.

*   *   *

I woke up to the sound of faint buzzing. Thinking it was a couple of annoying flies, I grabbed either end of the open hammock and closed it shut, hoping to keep out the little pests. They didn't go away though. Cracking open the material and peeking through the open seam, noting the light color of the evening sky, I immediately discovered a black swarm of buzzing mosquitoes above the opening of my hammock. Instantly, I brought one of my hands to my face, feeling around for itching bumps, but found nothing. It seemed none had made their way in.

Getting out would be another issue I'd need to solve. There wasn't any reason to get up right now, unless I was hungry or needed to pee, which I didn't. Instead, I looked beyond their brownish cloud and up to the sky to gauge the hour. It was that light shade of pink cotton candy that indicated it was probably somewhere around six or seven o'clock.

I could hear Sarah and Gretchen talking in muted voices to each other through their hammocks. "Hey," I said, studying mosquitoes with annoyance. "What time is it?"

Sarah answered first. "Uh, I don't know. I don't have my watch or phone on me."

"Me neither," Gretchen said. "Do we maybe wanna eat something soon?"

"Sure. Sarah and I both brought stove stuff in case there's anything you or the guys want to cook. I've got a some cups of ramen in case you want one," I said.

At the risk of sitting up head-first into a dark cloud of mosquitoes, I rolled out of my hammock and onto the floor. More skeeters than we anticipated began zipping around my ears and eyes with their buggy little bodies, and I suddenly felt the massive weight of my bladder pressing against my abdomen.

"You guys go ahead. I gotta pee really quick," I said to the two of them as I swatted mosquitoes away. The two of them were already on their feet and waiting for me. I dashed over to a nearby tree that offered just enough privacy between my exposed pelvis and the guys at the campsite. Then I squatted against the bark, bar-assed with my shorts around my ankles, and let sweet release take over. The trick was to angle your feet away from the tree so you wouldn't pee into your shorts. It was only when I was halfway done that I felt a million little flies buzzing underneath me.

Oh, no.

Dozens of little pins and needles began biting my cheeks and the surrounding area in the six remaining seconds I had left to pee. I was internally screaming at my body to hurry up so I could close the gate, but it only wanted to continue streaming at its own leisurely pace.

As soon as I managed to yank up my shorts, I hoped to *God* I didn't trap any of those buzzing fuckers inside between my ass and the lining of my shorts. It wasn't until I scrambled out of there and into the protection of Sarah's and my tent that I could cook in peace. Ignoring her odd stare, I chose to focus on lighting the little propane stove just outside of our half-zipped tent flap to heat up water so I could eat my ramen in peace. Not long after, I began to scratch my ass like a madman and, inevitably, explained to Sarah what had happened.

"Too bad we didn't bring itch cream along," she sighed, looking at me with a mix of pity and amusement.

Tired, itchy, and convinced that I'd just contracted malaria in the worst way possible, I went to bed.

It was only seven-fifteen.

*   *   *

Hiking back always felt much longer to me than hiking out. Maybe it was because you had the view or the campsite at the end to look forward to. It was no different than starting out on a road trip, right? You grabbed your drinks, got your tunes, and daydreamed the whole way there about what was to come. Then on the way back, you wished the drive was about half the length it actually was so you could get back home to familiarity again.

We all left in a huff that morning (mostly me), done with the bullshit of the trail and Frank's stupid directions. We were tired, hungry, exhausted, and, especially in my case, thoroughly bitten. Sarah's pack had lightened significantly since we used up more than half the water gallon she brought yesterday for cooking and replenishing our water bottles. Crossing the river and the creek didn't seem as big of a deal this time. It seemed to have died down a bit since yesterday, but that certainly didn't make it any less cold.

The sun baked us for most of the hike, despite our relatively early start, allowing us to dry out quickly enough. That was the difference between the Northwest and the Midwest—here, they didn't have thick, wet heat, only dry. That meant it wasn't such a chore to breathe, making the hike much more manageable.

We didn't talk much on the way back, keeping a lot of our thoughts to ourselves. I could feel myself growing more and more irritated with each step back in the direction we came. I'd already *seen* that shoreline, I'd already *crossed* that creek, I'd already *passed* those campsites…I just wanted to go *home*. The hike did nothing to ease my mental burdens, especially as we got toward the end.

Why did Frank have to be such an ass? Why couldn't we have stopped at one of those earlier campsites? What right did he have to pick on Sarah and me like that back at the ranger station? How could a ranger have given us the wrong directions?

I was done.

I wanted to give up my legs, my efforts, and my frustrations, and simply not exist in this moment. I wanted to have one of those magic remotes that Adam Sandler had in that movie *Click* and just fast-forward through this awful part of the journey.

When there were only a few miles left of the trail, both guys ditched us and increased their pace to get back to the car more quickly.

"Hey, don't they know that they can't sit in the car if they don't have the keys?" I asked Sarah.

She nodded, her tanned summer skin glistening with sweat. "Probably. Do you wanna run up there and throw them to him? Hey, Travis!" Sarah began to shout.

I shook my head. "No, no, no, it's okay! You don't need to do that. I wouldn't have the energy to run up there anyway. They'll just have to wait. I'm tired and cranky."

"You wanna pick up the pace just a bit so we can get back to the car sooner?" she asked.

I groaned. "Yes."

She turned to Gretchen next. "Hey, is it cool if we pick up the pace a bit?"

"Yeah, sure," she said, chocolate ringlets scrunched up into a loose bun on top of her head, probably to cool off the back of her neck.

They were in much better spirits than me. I was dirty, tired, bitten, cold, hungry, and a little sunburnt with a floppy, greasy ponytail falling out of my baseball hat. It felt more like a tail, actually. At this point, I convinced myself that I didn't need my legs anymore. They were Mother Earth's now. Everything about me was Her property—my thoughts, my pulse, my hip flexors, and the soles of my feet. I was sacrificing them for Her.

"How much farther?" I shouted to Gretchen and Sarah. I had fallen fifteen feet behind them and had been watching them walk side-by-side, engaged in casual conversation.

Sarah spoke. "About two miles."

"*FUCK!*"

The word echoed through the barren trees and off the dirt path as it left my mouth, not caring who heard it—child or adult. Wild laughter erupted from the two of them. In fact, they started laughing so hard that they had to stop to bend over.

"Lauren!" Gretchen wheezed. "I've never heard you talk like that!"

"Me either!" added Sarah, clutching her chest.

The corner of my mouth cracked into a smile as I approached them. I didn't want it to, but I couldn't help myself. It was a little funny. "I'm pissed and I wanna go *home!*"

"I'm sorry," Sarah laughed, throwing her messy, tangled braid back and straightening herself up. "We'll be back before you know it. I promise."

Composing herself, Gretchen added, "Yeah, just pretend there's only one mile left."

"Well, no, that's worse! Then I'll finish a mile and not be done!" I complained.

"Then break it up in your head—two miles is only two one miles put together."

That worked to a point. Then I just gave up and endured the rest of the walk, which oddly seemed to work better. I didn't think anymore, I didn't ache anymore, all I did was walk.

Coming around the dusty straightaway we started on, we saw the guys talking against the side of my car.

"Hey, there they are!" they cheered with their arms in the air. They looked much smaller without their packs on, lighter. "You're almost done!"

"How long you guys been waiting there?" Sarah called out.

"'Bout ten minutes," one of them shouted back.

I pulled out the car keys from one of the side pockets of my back, hoping it would unlock from this far away so they could put their bags in. From a distance, I saw a pop in the white trunk.

"Thank you!"

The three of us finally reached the car, exhausted and thankful. We had hiked sixteen miles.

It wasn't often I put myself in the way of this kind of challenge. It was horrifically, torturously, and infuriatingly wonderful. The only thing I could think to say about this character-building experience was a simple and honest four-letter word:

Fuck.

CHAPTER 10

...◆ ◆ ◆ ◆...

It didn't take long for me to become acquainted with Tyler and Dorian. Tyler stood out among the housekeeping group with his bright ginger hair and sky-blue eyes. Over the course of the season, I watched Dorian's short, curly hair turn into a style I could only attribute to a true "mountain man"—scruffy and wild. The end of every curl jutted out from underneath his Patagonia hat, whenever he wore it, impatient with the sudden constraint.

After work, they both made plans to do Avalanche Peak, a four-and-a-half-mile hike thirty minutes east, and invited Gretchen and me to tag along. We were all working and going as our own group would be both easy and convenient since we were operating on the same schedule. We planned on doing the usual: finishing up our duties as early as we could, heading over to the Employee Dining Room for dinner, then changing into our hiking clothes and heading out.

I'd just gotten off my nice, relaxing weekend when I shuffled into the hotel's conference room on the second floor at eight o'clock in the morning, clothed in my ugly, striped housekeeping uniform. Reaching the top of the crimson stairs, rounding the corner and stepping inside, I noticed the room was filled with an unfamiliar cluster of people. They were all waiting around, confused and not sure if they were in the right place. They looked like they might've been work-travel students from Asia. We'd gotten a few international employees already as we were nearing July, peak tourism season, so this was a good thing. Assuming they'd be training today, we could finish almost double the rooms in half the time with their help.

I managed to snag a spot on the back wall where I stood until Dorian came by with a list of highlighted pink and yellow room assignments for me. The more pink you had, the harder day it'd be because those were rooms that needed a full cleaning. The more yellow you had, the easier it'd be; those were rooms that were still occupied and only needed a little sprucing up. Whoever gave you your list also indicated they'd be your inspector for the day.

"You're gonna be really happy with me," he said, handing mine to me.

Glancing at my list, I noticed all the yellow highlights. Looking back up at him with gratitude in my eyes, I sighed. "Man, you're awesome. What do I owe you for this?"

"A hike at Avalanche Peak with me, Connor, and Gretchen," he grinned.

I gave him a thumbs up. "You got it." Looking down at my list again, I noticed a name in the top right corner right under mine.

"Hey, wait a minute. What's this?" I said, pointing to the name *Steven* scribbled right above my index finger.

"Oh, yeah!" he said, slightly louder this time as he navigated the crowd in search of the next team member to give them their list. "That's your trainee for today!"

Not a second later, Claire, the main housekeeping manager, then strode inside, clipboard and walkie-talkie in hand. "Hey, y'aaaaall!" she said, announcing her presence for all to hear.

Claire looked the same every day: platinum blonde with brown roots hair piled onto her head in a fan bun with a black dress, black cardigan, black stockings, and black combat boots. Her husky blue eyes were coated in a ring of chunky black mascara.

"Hiii...heyyy..." the crowd muttered in a jumbled greeting.

"Man, you guys are zapped this morning," she commented, getting organized at the head of the conference table on the other side of the room.

After Claire came in both Mary and Danica, with their clipboards and radios, followed by all the housekeeping inspectors behind them. It was like a procession.

I never realized how diverse our managerial staff was:

Mary was a Corporate Marley.

Danica was a bubbly older sister.

And Claire was borderline goth.

"Okay, a few quick announcements," Claire said, presenting us with miscellaneous updates around the Lake Hotel. "First off, some of you have been filling up the soap bottles in the showers with water instead of soap. I don't wanna tell you twice; y'all *need* to be using the bags for those. We've got plenty. I don't want NPS coming across something like that during inspections." She was referring to the liter-sized bags of shampoo, conditioner, and body wash we squeezed into the bottles mounted on the walls of the showers. People often skipped refills because it either slowed them down or they were being lazy. NPS was the National Park Service, and it was not uncommon for them to pop in unannounced at the hotel on occasion to conduct random inspections. The managers hated this, probably because it made them feel less in control.

Claire and Danica rattled off a few more announcements before distributing keys. A gray plastic bucket of coiled keyrings with tags sat on the table, where one of the managers usually threw them out to their respective housekeepers for the day.

Danica looked at her clipboard, reading off names as she began digging her hand into the bucket and tossing them across the table to various people.

"Gretchen?"

"Over here!"

Toss.

"Tyler?"

"Here."

Toss.

Next, we went outside to the front of the hotel. Everyone got up, lists, keys, radios, and clipboards in hand, and climbed the two flights down to the main hotel lobby, where a fair number of guests watched us walk out the front doors. I felt like I was on a class field trip in my matching housekeeping uniform.

We formed a circle in front of the hotel sunroom, right by where the driveway curved around into a U-shape under the awning.

Claire spoke first. "All right, who's gonna be our team leader?"

"I will!" one of the more outgoing inspectors piped up, stepping into the middle of the circle. "Okay, cool, let's start off with some arm stretches!" he announced, reaching one arm across his chest and holding it in place with his other hand.

We stood still and unmoving for about fifteen seconds before being instructed to switch.

"Vacuums!" he said, transitioning into a deep lunge with one foot in front of him and the other stretched behind. He extended one of his arms forward and moved it back and forth like, well, a vacuum.

"Ooh, I love these!" Danica piped up, taking a deep stance in her bright patterned sundress.

Doing these stretches in public made me want to die inside every time. It felt like I was being put on display, as if I'd somehow gotten roped into walking in the Macy's Thanksgiving Day Parade against my will or something. Looking over my shoulder I saw an amused, elderly couple watching us from inside the sunroom, smiling and—oh, Lord—taking pictures.

The stretching, or *team bonding* as they called it, went on for another ten minutes before we were finally released to our respective places—the hotel, Sandpiper, or the cabins.

I turned around, looking for an unfamiliar face that could've been my trainee, when I spotted a greasy-looking guy. He was tall and lanky with moppy brown hair and a slight curve in his shoulder blades that jutted his neck out a little, sort of like Shaggy from Scooby-Doo. He looked to be about sixteen or seventeen.

"Hey," I greeted, walking up to him. "Are you Steven?"

He turned around. "Yeah, are you Lauren?"

"That's me. We're gonna be working out in cabins today, which is on the other side of the hotel and down the big hill." I pulled the assignment list out of the front pocket of my striped uniform shirt for a brief review. "Lucky for you, we've got a pretty light day today, only three due-outs and eight occupieds. All that means is we have three rooms to fully clean and eight to partially clean, so it should go by pretty fast. Plus, we've got a slew of new workers that just came in this morning."

He pulled up his sagging pants with one of his skeletal hands as I spoke. I noticed it was bandaged in a flesh-colored compression wrap around his wrist.

"Hey, what happened to your hand?" I asked, my eyebrows turning upward in concern.

He threw a quick glance over his shoulder then tugged his sleeve up with a smirk. "BMX."

"BMX?"

"Yeah, BMX biking," he chuckled. "I was in this competition a few weeks ago and it got a little crazy. Pretty sure it's broken. It's a good thing they don't know about it, though," he said, referring to managers who had already retreated back inside the hotel.

The expression on my face must not have phased him. He didn't seem to mind how concerning that was, much less how that would affect our performance today.

"Doesn't it hurt?"

He shrugged. "Nah, not really. I've just been taking some Tylenol for it, so it's all good."

I could feel a hard line of concern develop between my scrunched eyebrows. "Can you move it?"

"Sure can," he said, demonstrating a strained 360° motion.

I opened my mouth, thinking about my next words. "So then...it's not broken. Just sprained it looks like. Right?"

Steven shrugged again. "I guess so."

Forcing myself to lighten my stare, I gave a quick smile, then took us through the back door of the hotel, across the large parking lot, and down the long descending asphalt to catch up with a few other RAs I'd gotten to know over the past month. I figured it'd be helpful for Steven to meet them since he'd most likely be working with some of them, especially if he got placed out in cabins after training.

Once at the cabin office at the base of the hill, where multiple bins were stacked in vertical piles in the middle of the floor, I showed him what our key number meant. "Ours says 3C, so we gotta find the bins with that label. If you find one, you'll find them all, unless someone stacked one in the wrong pile. Make sense?" Then we loaded our respective bins and a half-decent vacuum into the first cart we could grab before making the long trek back up to the top of the hill.

"This way," I explained, hauling the mule cart behind me, "it's easier to grab supplies since you'll be working your way down anyway. The arrangement of the cabins can be confusing, too, so no worries if you have trouble keeping all the cabin numbers straight."

Tyler was looking at something across the street, distracted.

"Okay?" I asked, a bit peeved.

He turned around, meeting my eyes with a nod. "Yeah, got it."

I eyed him carefully, being as intentional as possible with both my gaze and directions, hoping he'd keep his attention on me while I had him. "So, our section is the five hundreds—501, 502, 503—and they're all on this side of the street. Six hundreds are on the other. We're not cleaning all the cabins on this side, maybe a third of them, since we have some RAs tackling this section with us."

"Mhm."

"And even though we only have three due-out today, the pink rooms on our list, we're starting with those first just to get them out of the way."

"Okay."

Even though he was looking at me, I could tell his thoughts were elsewhere.

Walking up to our first room at the top, cabin 509, I demonstrated how to approach the door. Knocking once, I chimed, "Hello, housekeeping."

No answer.

I knocked again. "Hello, housekeeping."

No answer.

I knocked a third time, this time announcing, "Housekeeping coming in," before unlocking the door with my brass key on its coiled chain.

Opening the door and peering inside, it didn't look too bad. Both double beds would need to be changed and some of the amenities would need to be restocked, but overall, it looked about as average as any other checked-out room.

Leaving the door open, we stepped inside. "Okay," I said, "how about you strip all the beds and I'll go around and start gathering all the towels and trash?"

Steven shrugged. "Okay."

"So what you're gonna do is separate the pillowcases from the regular bedsheet. We do that to help out the people up north in Mammoth who do all the laundry," I explained, stripping off the kitschy, fish-patterned comforters and placing them in a nearby chair to help get him started.

"Sounds good," he nodded.

I played some music on my phone, something I regularly did, and began to find my rhythm with the room. It hadn't been more than five minutes when I noticed a bit of a smell. Concerned, I checked the toilet, the base of the toilet, the shower, the trash cans, and the sink but couldn't trace the origin. It's like it was drifting or something. Maybe something happened to the sheets of the bed. Whatever it was, it quickly grew undeniably potent—sour, rancid, nose hair-curling.

I turned the corner from the bathroom I was in to check the sheets Steven was handling. From what I could tell, they looked fine, so I stepped outside to grab a couple of fresh bath towels (and air) when, in passing, I noticed just how stringy Steven's hair was and all the acne spots sprinkled across his face.

Suspicious, I walked over to the bed that had already been stripped behind him. I inhaled before speaking and instantly felt nauseous. "Here you go," I smiled, dropping the sheets onto the mattress. "Let me know when you're done and I'll show you how to make the beds."

"Thanks."

It was him. It was *totally* him.

Steven had a seriously rancid case of body odor.

I walked back out to the cart again, desperate to fill my lungs with air. Composing myself, I grabbed a handful of towels before stepping back inside, rushing to the other side of the room and around the corner where the bathroom was, in an attempt to separate my nose from his smell.

"So," I said, clearing my throat of the lingering odor, "are you staying in any of the dorms around here?"

"Nah, I live in an RV with my girlfriend over at Bridge Bay. We're engaged and trying for a baby."

My eyes popped out of my head. *WHAT? A baby?! He* is *a baby, he can't even wash himself!* Engagements were one thing but *babies?* Babies were a whole other ballgame. Thank God I was hidden by the walls of the bathroom, or he would've seen my shocked expression, wide-eyed and slack-jawed.

I composed myself as much as I could before picking up the pile of dirty towels outside the bathroom door and bringing them over to his pile of pillowcases in the main room. Speechless, I gave a tight smile. "Congratulations."

He was sitting on one of the stripped beds, stinking it up with his clothes. I cringed thinking about the guests who'd be lying on top of that spot. Turning around, I grabbed one of the clean sheets from the pile on the second bed and began shaking it out from its crisp fold. Creased lines decorated it like a checkerboard. Thankfully, Steven took the hint and got up from his sitting position so I could drape it over the mattress he was on. Once it was centered the way I wanted it, I began tucking the excess under the mattress so it served as the base sheet.

Steven gleamed while he talked. "Yeah, my girlfriend's been wanting a baby for, like, forever, so we've been trying for a while now."

I didn't even want to envision that. The thought of the two of them going at it almost made me puke a little inside of my mouth. I swallowed hard, pushing it all down. "That's n-nice."

"Hey, they didn't tell you I was seventeen, did they?" he asked, randomly changing the subject.

I paused to look at him and frowned. "No…?"

"'Kay, good," he said with a sigh, flicking his head to the side to get his shaggy hair out of his eyes. "I just wrote eighteen down on my application and hoped they wouldn't question it or anything."

I nodded slowly, concerned, wondering how in the world he got through the initial check-in up north at Gardiner. They asked for ID there. He had to have used a fake.

Something about Steven didn't sit right with me, and it wasn't just that he lied about his age, stunk to high heavens, was working with a "broken" hand, and had been trying for a fucking *baby*...it was deeper. It's like something was missing in him; some of the pieces weren't there, not all the gears were turning. I had no idea what it was, but something was very clearly just "off."

By noon, I had the worst headache of my life. My heart leaped when I saw the usual group—Tyler, Gretchen, and Dorian—heading up the hill for lunch through the window of the cabin we were cleaning. We were finishing our third room when I suggested to Steven that we break for food, which he didn't seem to have a problem with. Bursting out of the cabin door, overcome by the plethora of fresh air, I began gulping heaps of it into my lungs as I ran to catch up with them, practically sprinting.

"Hey guys," I greeted, out of breath and grateful to be in their presence.

"Hey," smiled Gretchen, freckles blooming across her nose and cheeks, before giving me a funny look as if she knew something was up. "You okay?"

"Yeah, I'm good," I coughed.

"Lauren, what rooms have you and Steven done so far?" Dorian asked in his grounded, baritone voice, leaning forward to see me better. His thick, dark curls were doing flips off his scalp, dancing around in the warm summer breeze.

"We just finished our last due-out in 513. We've got some occupieds left and that's it."

He extended his hand out for me to high-five. "You're awesome. We've been crushing it today," he said, referring to the RAs he was leading. "By the way, how's Steven doing?"

"Omigod, he *reeks*."

Everyone looked over at me with surprised and puzzled looks.

"It's so awful," I continued. "I have this massive headache from it right now."

"Did you tell him?" Dorian asked.

"Did I tell him that he stunk? No, I didn't know how. I didn't want to embarrass him!"

"You should tell management about it. Tell Claire," Tyler suggested.

"Actually, I'll just tell her when I go up there for our meeting this afternoon with the other inspectors," Dorian said. "Jesus, doesn't he shower? I kept smelling something in one of your rooms I inspected, but I didn't know it was *him*. I just thought it was from the guests who were there."

I shrugged, totally at a loss. "I don't know, but he said he was living in an RV with his girlfriend over at Bridge Bay, and they've been trying for a baby. Oh, and he's *seventeen*!"

Every single one of their jaws dropped, shocked. Gretchen almost spit out her water from the gulp she took from her Nalgene.

"*What?*"

"*Seventeen?*"

"A *baby?*"

"Yes!" I said, leaning in and wide-eyed, answering each of their responses. "And he supposedly 'broke' his wrist, which is why it's bandaged up, but I think it's just sprained." I motioned air quotes around *broke*.

Dorian shook his head in agitation. "Yeah, okay, I'm gonna tell Claire. He shouldn't even be working. He's a liability, dude. If Terrego found out he had a broken wrist, he'd be entitled to worker's comp and, of course, they'd be pissed about having to pay that."

We walked inside the hotel to clock out for lunch. "Sounds good. Let me know if I need to do anything," I said.

"By the way, y'all, I'm gonna set a timer on my phone for lunch since we're all arriving at the same time," Gretchen offered, honoring Terrego's time allotment of thirty-five minutes and no more.

We all shook our heads in agreement.

"Will do," Dorian said before giving a big shrug. "Hey, the Finer Things Club, right? Rancid guys and cleaning supplies. We're suave as fuck."

Everyone burst out laughing, something we all probably needed.

*   *   *

Steven and I finished cleaning the rest of our assigned rooms, all eleven, and helped a couple of other room attendants with theirs. Then we trekked back over to the cabin office and awaited a signature on our room assignment sheets before grabbing our stuff and leaving. Only me, Steven, Gretchen, and Tyler remained, so Dorian, one of the two inspectors in the cabins, took the initiative to radio the other inspectors around the area if anyone else needed help.

"Dorian to all Lake Hotel inspectors, anyone need any RA help in the hotel or Sandpiper?" he asked, strong and melodic.

We all held our breath, hoping no one else needed us. If they did, we'd have to clean who knows how many more rooms. If they didn't, that increased our chances of having another early day, something we always hoped for.

"Nope," one anonymous voice crackled through.

"Not here," said another.

"Good on my end," a third chimed in.

A few more no's came through before Dorian clipped his radio onto his front pants pocket, concluding with pride, "Looks like we're done."

All of us cheered and checked our watches, then again, to make sure we were reading it correctly: two-thirty p.m., the earliest we'd ever finished—approximately three hours earlier than our average finishing time.

By the time we'd made it to the second-floor housekeeping office, Sanchez, a Hispanic–Native American worker about our age with long black hair and beautiful olive skin, was already there sitting at the reception desk with his black working shoes kicked up. Rumor had it he actually pet a bison once.

"Hey guys, what's up?" he asked with a big smile on his face, showing two short, pointed canines on either side of his cheeks. He held out his hand for Dorian to slap, one of those brotherly handshakes guys sometimes do.

"Hey, we just finished out in the cabins and are checking in with whoever's in there to hopefully get off early," Dorian said, motioning to the cracked door a few steps ahead.

Sanchez nodded us over. "Yeah, sounds like everyone's getting off early. A couple of people have already come in. Go on ahead, I think Mary's back in there," he said, holding his hands up to his head, referring to the large coil of ginger dreadlocks she always kept on top of her head.

Dorian responded with a quiet groan and an eye roll.

The rest of us stayed back while he headed over toward the door. He looked back, just before opening the door, to see Sanchez giving him an over-the-top grin and a thumbs-up. Then Dorian turned to me, motioning for me to come over. "You can talk to her about your *help*," he hinted. Steven wasn't around but he was being careful of his presence anyway.

"I thought you guys talked about it at the inspectors' meeting earlier this afternoon," I said, a worried look bleeding across my face.

He shook his head. "Haven't had it yet. It's an early day."

As I walked over, he gave two knocks on the door and eased it open with a hand. Mary looked up, her smokey purple eyeshadow catching my attention, as she typed rapidly across the clunky, white keyboard. She had chopsticks shoved into her dreadlock bun today, sporting an oriental theme.

"Hey guys, how's it going?" she greeted in a honeyed voice.

Dorian spoke first. "Pretty good. We finished the cabins and Sam, the other inspector, is with the RAs downstairs sorting recycling. Sandpiper and the hotel said they didn't need help, so we're here to check in with you." He then lowered his voice and leaned in to her slightly. "Also, Lauren had a bit of an issue with her trainee she'd like to tell you about."

Mary glanced up at me from her dinosaur computer screen, which she had mostly concentrated on throughout Dorian's update. "Oh? Okay, shut the door. What happened?"

"Well," I started, easing it closed and trying to find the right words. I shot a side glance at Dorian next to me, silently asking for help. "Uh, well, Steven has this...thing that was hindering my work performance, which is...um, his odor."

She stared at me. "His odor?"

Dorian spoke up again, briefly. "The guy reeks. I could smell it in every one of their rooms I inspected."

That seemed to get her attention. Mary looked back at me with a perplexed expression, something I'd never seen her wear before. "Really?"

I looked down at my feet briefly before looking back up at her with a shallow nod. "He also claimed to be seventeen," I added.

Her purple eyes shot open. "Seventeen?"

"And his wrist was bandaged up; he said it was broken."

Mary stood completely still, wide-eyed and at a loss. "Really," she said again, this time more serious. The tone in her voice had dropped to something much more real and less sing-songy.

Finally, she leaned back into her chair. "Okay, I'll call him in before he leaves today and have a talk with him. In the meantime, you guys can…" she trailed off, searching the office for ideas, "take a couple of blue rags with some spray and polish the doorknobs on this floor. Bring in the others and I'll give them assignments, too."

I saw something in Dorian's expression change out of the corner of my eye. "Thanks," he said as he left the little closet of an office and past the small cluster of RAs.

"Next," I could hear Mary announce from behind us.

"Fuck this," he mumbled, once we were down the carpeted hallway with our blue rags and ambiguous yellow spray in hand. "Shining doorknobs? Are you *kidding* me? If management's always wanting us to finish early, why the hell are they keeping us? Everyone's done. There's literally nothing left to do."

We were in the west wing of the hotel where the ceilings were much higher and the hallway was much wider. Lining the left side of the hall was a neat, freckled row of blue and white bags. This wing looked different from the east because of a renovation that happened decades ago to expand the number of hotel rooms.

"This is pretty stupid," I agreed. "The only reason she's keeping us is because the other attendants aren't completely finished with their shit. It's just recycling, it takes ten minutes tops to do that."

"Well yeah, and because inspectors aren't supposed to get dismissed before the RAs," he said, shaking his head in frustration. "Had I known Mary would be in the office, I would've just had us hang out in the cabin office until Claire was available. She's not as strict on that."

Silence fell between us for a while before he spoke again. "If we have to clean doorknobs for an hour, I don't know what I'm gonna do."

"Maybe it won't take that long," I said. "We'll just kill time, half-assing the doorknobs, until we see the rest of the room attendants heading to the office to check out."

We turned right at the end of the hallway and worked our way toward the end of the hall, out of any manager's line of vision. Picking one of the two sides to start on, we began gliding our blue rags over each bronze-painted doorknob, not actually cleaning them, just so we could say we were doing it if anyone caught us.

In the end, we were only robbed of about twenty minutes. The rest of the room attendants and inspectors finished their cleaning, recycling, and restocking duties before officially being released by Mary. It really was just about keeping us busy until the rest *literally* finished.

We officially clocked out at three-fifteen, barely enough time to spare for a late afternoon hike.

CHAPTER 11

...◆◆◆...

Steven wasn't at work the next day. It wasn't until Dorian brought it up at the end of work before clocking out that he confirmed my suspicion—Steven had been fired. Couldn't say I was all that surprised.

We restocked and reported the last of our rooms to our inspectors who were either typing numbers onto the old computer in the back or examining our bins. The usual. Then we walked to the EDR for a surprisingly more upscale meal of fried catfish and eggplant parmesan. A lot of the group was already there. I walked up with my tray when I heard Gretchen mention something about a dance.

"What?" I said, dropping my plate onto the table. "Lake's hosting a dance?"

"Yeah," she said, pulling her curls up into a ponytail using the scrunchy on her wrist. "Heard some people in the cabin office talking about it today."

"Oh. Well, where was I when that happened?" I wondered aloud.

"What are you guys talking about?" asked Tyler, who had been occupied with stacking packets of ketchup on top of each other like a miniature Jenga game. His hair almost matched the *Heinz* logo.

Gretchen filled him in. "There's gonna be a dance in a couple of weeks, mid-July."

"We should pregame," he said.

"What's going on?" asked Dorian, bringing his attention over to us from a separate conversation he was having with a couple of the others.

"There's gonna be a dance in July," Tyler repeated.

"We should pregame," he said.

Tyler rolled his eyes. "That's what I just said."

Pretty soon the whole table got to talking about it. It was a ranch theme and would be in the employee rec center of the Lake Lodge. Despite the two weeks of notice we had, everyone began planning out the details, like whose room we'd hang out in and when we would want to go, sparking obvious interest among the group.

Personally, I liked the idea of dances more than the real thing. More often than not, the music sucked, the dancing sucked, the atmosphere sucked, and I always found myself feeling worse off than I did initially. People wanted to seem cool, at least in my experience, so they'd become absorbed with getting the right person's attention or letting loose to the point that it became hard to relate to them anymore. I'd always wanted to have fun at dances, but it just never seemed to work out that way for me.

Dinner began wrapping up as the usual kitchen crew came out with their cleaning buckets and wash rags, initiating our walk back home to the dorms. I was walking with Sarah in the back when, somehow, talk of books came up.

"I'm reading John Muir right now," Dorian mentioned. "Gretchen, isn't that what you're reading?"

She shook her head. "No, I haven't read Muir yet."

"I tried *Walden* by Henry David Thoreau and thought it was pretty good," said Candice, her messy bun flopping around with every step she took. "I love his poeticism. I've always wanted to write like that, but I've never been able to get that same effect with my stuff."

Without thinking, I stepped forward and blurted out, "You write poetry?"

She turned and I could see something in her face melt into immediate regret. "Oh...yeah, but like it's pretty low-key stuff. Not a lot of people know about it." She turned around, signaling the end of our little chat.

"I write poetry, too," I said, stepping closer.

"Cool."

"You can read some of my stuff if you want," I added. "I'm pretty private with it too, but I'd like to get another person's perspective on it if you're open to it."

Candice looked over her shoulder, eyeing me like she was searching for something. "All right," she finally said as we approached the outside steps leading up to the second floor of Pelican. I hadn't noticed the other half walking over to Osprey across the road. "I'll be over in ten."

The sound of the knock at the door came with a pink spiral notebook and Bic pen. There weren't any good places to sit, so we plopped down on the blue-carpeted floor, between the two twin beds. Sarah was sitting on hers, preparing to start another watercolor painting, casually listening.

Unsure of how to exactly proceed, we both shared little, short bits we'd written, gauging the other person's interest. Sharing any personal journal entries, poetry or otherwise, made a person vulnerable. We might as well have been exposing our soft, white underbellies, hoping one wouldn't slaughter the other with judgment, unwarranted criticism, or worse, apathy.

"I don't have a title for this one," I said, "but it's a short little poem: I'm a work in progress, a peculiar sight, / a symphonic star, a fire of white, / preparing myself for my own supernova, / when I fall into me and explode into light."

Candice looked at me with white eyes through her thick-framed glasses. "I *love* that. I absolutely *love* that."

I looked at her, my cheeks feeling redder by the second. "Really?"

"Yes, it really speaks to me," she said, smiling.

I leaned back against the desk that sat along the wall between Sarah's bed and mine. Its side drawers dug into my spine, but I didn't mind. "I was worried it sounded too clunky, you know, too many words happening all at once."

"No, I don't think so," she said, shaking her head. "It had a pretty good balance to it in my opinion."

I sighed. "Thanks. Okay, your turn."

"Okay, this one's called 'Red,'" Candice said, taking a deep breath in.

It was about an experience much deeper than I could personally understand. She wrote in seasons, instead of sensations like I do. This one sounded like autumn and winter. It was a feeling of defeat and endings, expressed in both a beautiful and melancholy way.

"Wow." I breathed. "I could tell just how much emotion that held for you."

She nodded. "It was definitely a significant time in my life. I don't want to go much deeper than the poem, but…"

"Yeah, don't worry about it. It sounded like a very vulnerable time in your life, and I definitely wouldn't want to feel like I'm prying."

It took a solid hour of sharing for us to exhaust all of our immediate work. It was then I was reminded of a book I read right before coming to Yellowstone that, I think, expressed exactly what we were trying to say in our own writing. So, I used his name, hoping to lure her into another poetry session later on. I didn't want this to be our one and only chance to actually get to know each other. I wanted to know more about who she was after hours.

"What's it called again?" Candice asked.

"*The One Life We're Given* by Mark Nepo. Next time we meet up, I'll bring it with me," I smiled.

"Sure," she agreed, "let's grab coffee after work on Thursday and we'll bring some of our other journals."

After that, I swear to you, I could feel my heart sigh—I didn't realize it had been holding its breath.

Finally being able to speak like a poet, like a writer, to another person held so much meaning for me. The only connections I ever felt were to the words in the pages of my books, spoken by brilliant authors, who knew what it meant to look at life up close and ask the deeper questions: *What do you really want to say? What did that experience really mean for you? Who do you really want to say those things to?*

It was like learning that there was such a thing as Santa Claus or the Tooth Fairy. I would no longer have to live my life shielding my thoughts and feelings. I could finally, *finally* share them with someone.

No longer was I alone.

*   *   *

Thursday finally came.

Candice and I walked up to the hotel from the cabins and toward the in-house deli. We both ordered a medium coffee and requested two pumps of hazelnut each. I saw Sarah, who was deep in the kitchen behind the counter, and gave her a wave.

"Isn't it a little late in the evening to be drinking coffee?" the guy behind the counter asked.

"We've got plans," retorted Candice.

He rolled his eyes. "That'll be six bucks."

Candice gave him a suspicious look. "Try again, doll. We get the forty percent discount, remember?"

He tapped some buttons on his screen, revising the cost of the order. "Three-sixty."

"Better," she said, after paying and swiping our cups from the counter.

Still in our uniforms, we walked outside the front entrance of the hotel, resisting the urge to look guests in the eye for fear of being asked for more towels or coffee. Down the long, U-shaped driveway and across the street, we found a little hidden lake shore with crystal clear waters behind a long patch of golden grass. It was the perfect temperature outside. I could feel the soft summer wind blowing against my face, breathing in that earthy perfume, and let the sun beat down on my skin.

We sat down, stripping our battered feet of their shoes and socks, and stuffed our feet under mounds of hot sand. I pulled out Mark Nepo from my drawstring bag, using my thumb to navigate through the heavily annotated and dog-eared pages. There, I began reading my favorite lines out of the book, letting his words swirl around the air between us.

I would occasionally pause to catch the wildflowers that had been pressed into the pages of the book so they wouldn't fall out. Sarah taught me to do that. *That way,* she'd said, *you always have something to look forward to.* To conserve the park's natural beauty, picking wildflowers was illegal, but we'd pick a few on our walks around the Lake area.

Mark's words were intended to console and heal the individual by opening them up to their own inner journey. Their pain, their suffering, their turmoil were further understood with simplicity and truth, two things that often scared the average person.

We were here and we were alive.

I could feel Candice looking at me as I read, hearing the exact thing she needed to hear at the exact moment she needed to hear it. She was still and seemed almost too scared to breathe.

"Wow," she whispered after I'd finished a few lines. "This guy's good. Do you mind if I borrow that book for a while?"

I smiled, shrugging. "Go for it."

"I'm really glad we're doing this," she said. "I didn't think there would be people out here who felt the way we did, you know? How we're deep and feeling people."

I knew. I really, really knew.

This is how we would occasionally spend our evenings after work, sometimes two or three times a week: we would have our journals and hazelnut coffee by the beach and talk about what it meant to live within our own profound human experience, to live the one life we were given.

CHAPTER 12

———— ··•✦•·· ————

I had about a month left in Yellowstone and had recently decided to extend my end date to early August instead of late July. I wanted to spend my twenty-first birthday out here with my friends, and if there was any place to get irredeemably drunk with your friends, it was in the middle of the Wyoming woods.

There was also a secret tradition where you were supposed to sign your name in Sharpie on the wall of the employee pub before leaving. It was secret because, naturally, you're not supposed to write in Sharpie on the walls, but to be fair, there was hardly a blank spot inside. The old wooden columns, walls, and even beams of the pub were covered in signatures from hundreds of employees since at least 1972, the oldest signature I'd seen yet.

One of my favorite markings was on the far side of the pub near the bartender's counter that read:

The Three Lies of Yellowstone:

    1. I'm not drinking tonight.

    2. "I love you."

    3. I'm never coming back.

The third one was circled, underlined, and had a drawing of an arrow pointing to it, presumably done by three different people over the years. Something about its blatant honesty was refreshing. I imagined some scruffy, intoxicated fairy dropping down on my shoulder and whispering in my ear with a harsh gruff, "Listen, kid. If there are three things you need to know about this place, it's these."

I mentioned this to a few people when we were hanging out in the hotel sunroom after work to listen to the quartet play, one of our favorite things to do in the evenings. "I extended my end date," I said, sitting on the floor by the coffee table while Dorian and a couple of other people sat in the maroon wingback chairs.

"Ooh, Terrego's gonna like you," Dorian said, his curly hair flipping out from underneath his Patagonia hat. He was holding a glass of red wine in his hand while he spoke. "If you stay all the way through your contract, you get a bonus."

"When did you extend it till?" Tyler asked, next to me.

"August eighth," I said, turning back to everyone. "You guys gonna be around? My birthday's on the fifth. We could all hang out at the pub together."

Tyler looked at me with his bright blue eyes. "Yours is the fifth? Mine is the third, we should definitely celebrate!"

One of the other inspectors I'd seen around, Sam, spoke in a husky voice, "Oh man, I'll be gone by then! Try a shot of 'Sex on the Beach' for me. It's my favorite!"

"I'll be gone then, too," Dorian said, taking a sip of his wine. "I think Candice should still be around, though. She'll be one of the few left at that point, I think."

"Oh, gotcha," I said, feeling a little bummed. "That's okay, yeah, Candice and Tyler and I can all celebrate together then."

The quartet was right in the middle of the room playing a cover of "Paradise" by Coldplay when Dorian's roommate came by. He worked as a bartender in the hotel and was on his shift. "Hey, guys, what's goin' on?" he said, walking over.

"Not much, just enjoying tonight's ambiance," Dorian said.

He nodded. "Speaking of which, whaddya guys want to drink? On the house. Dorian, I see you're taken care of," he said, motioning to his glass of red wine.

The bar was right behind us, positioned between the open sunroom and the doors of the dining room on the other side, where guests could have a fancier experience. The table of the bar, a dark granite, looped all the way around what looked like a large China cabinet, chocolate wood, with a glass rack full of booze in the middle. Guests flooded it like moths to a light.

"Won't you get in trouble?" Sam, the inspector, asked.

He shrugged, his white sleeves brushing against his dark maroon vest. "Nah. It's so busy here tonight, my manager won't even know. C'mon, whatcha havin'?"

"Won't Claire or someone catch us?" I asked, concerned. I didn't want to suddenly have a problem with management and lose my job. "Didn't that one RA get caught last week for serving alcohol to underage girls at a party?"

"Yeah, she got fired," said Dorian.

Sam chimed in, the sound of her husky voice just barely audible over the noise of the crowd and quartet. "But the chances of Claire coming out here tonight and finding us exactly where we are are so slim. I mean, you're sitting on the floor on the very far side of the sunroom, hidden by two wingback chairs. She'd have to have eyes like a hawk to see that." Sam looked back at Dorian's roommate who was still waiting for orders. "I'll have a Sauvignon Blanc, please."

"A pinot noir for me," added Tyler.

Vince looked expectantly at me, along with everyone else. My ears began to heat up. *I'll be twenty-one next month,* I reasoned with myself. *Hypothetically, they couldn't nab me for being thirty-eight days away, right? Just do it.* I looked at Dorian's friend, allowing the knot in my stomach to dissipate. "Do you have Riesling?"

He nodded with a grin. "We do. I'll get you guys those drinks in just a bit," he said before turning back into the crowd.

The evening would be complete when the bartender came back with a tray of three glasses of wine, two white and one red. "Here you go," he said, giving each one to us individually. "Enjoy the night, guys! Take it easy, Dorian," he said before giving him a single pat on the shoulder.

There we all were, with our wine, a quartet, and a lovely evening view of the lake. At this moment, everything felt very right. I was exactly where I needed to be with the exact people I needed to be with. The clouds outside were fluffy and pink, indicative of the early evening. The lake the hotel faced was a glimmering sheet of blue glass, reflecting the various shades of pink and purple off its still waters.

I motioned out the window with my head, sipping my Riesling. "That's a pretty view. Almost unreal," I said.

They looked at the view, seeing the exact picture I saw, nodding in agreement.

"Heavenly," agreed Sam.

"Speaking of which," Dorian said, turning his glass around in a wide circle so the red liquid swirled around inside, "Why haven't you been hanging out with your God Squad people?"

"What do you mean? I hung out with Candice yesterday and I saw Sarah this morning," I responded, puzzled.

"No, I mean, don't you guys, like, go on retreats and stuff?"

I gave him a funny look. "I think they went to one in Gardiner not too long ago. Why?"

"Aren't you in the God Squad?"

"No."

For some reason, he looked very surprised. "You're *not?*"

"No, I've never been in ACMNP." I let out a short laugh at how taken aback he was.

Dorian stared at me in astonishment. "I could've sworn you were. Literally, this whole time, that's why I thought you were hanging out with Candice and Piper and Sarah and them so much."

"Well, Sarah's my roommate and, obviously, I work with Candice and Piper. They're just good friends I occasionally hang out with," I said, not sure why he was so surprised.

"Honestly, I thought that, too," added Tyler. His glass had diminished by a fourth.

"Why did you guys think I was in the God Squad?" I asked, though I knew the reason. It was because I was, and had always been, the nice girl.

Dorian shrugged. "I don't know, I just thought—"

"Oh, *shit,*" Sam interrupted, nearly spilling her drink. "Claire's here. Management, ten o'clock."

I looked behind the chairs in the direction she mentioned and saw her on the other end of the sunroom, striding toward the bar nearby. She was still wearing her platinum hair up in that messy fan bun, but this time, looked completely different—like she had a whole style outside of her work attire or something. Actually, she kind of looked like a hippie with her colorful headband and flowy, patterned pants. It was definitely different.

We all hushed our voices and hunched over, trying to hide our faces and attempting to look as small as possible. It didn't work. I don't know how she spotted us, but she changed direction from walking toward the bar to walking toward us. Not entirely knowing what to do, I stayed still and tried to think of a way to distract myself.

"Hey, guys," she greeted, her arctic blue eyes piercing through her thick black rings of mascara. Claire never ceased to intimidate me. Her stare was rigid, unmoving. "What's goin' on?" Her eyes flashed to the various glasses of wine on the table, particularly the two next to Tyler and me.

No one said anything at first. Dorian's voice was the first to break the silence among us, smooth and rational. "Just hangin' out. We came to listen to the quartet play tonight." We knew he had it in good with Claire because, supposedly, he once saw her cry in the office. I'd occasionally hear her bitch about work to him more than the other inspectors, maybe because she found him trustworthy. Either way, they had a solid inspector-manager relationship.

"Looks like you guys got some good drink choices here." Half of us nodded and the other half found something on the ground to stare at. "What are y'all havin'?" she asked, though we all knew the question was more meant for Tyler and me.

My stomach had dropped further than I ever thought possible. Being the truth-teller I am, I practically blurted out my answer. "Riesling."

If I was physically capable of kicking my own butt, I immediately would have.

Tyler had pushed his near-empty glass off to the side right before she came over, like a genius. He played it cool. "That was already here when I sat down. It's not mine."

Claire's intent stare iced me over completely. Really, if you painted me white, I could've been a Greek statue. A bitter taste formed on the back of my tongue as I prepared for the ax to drop. I was gonna be fired for underage drinking. No one moved. No one spoke.

"Well, enjoy your evening." She nodded. Then she turned away, disappearing back into the crowd as if this whole thing hadn't happened. A minute went by before anyone said anything. My eyes were wide as I turned to look at Tyler, clueless. Was I fired? Did I still have my job? I thought I was safe, though it was hard to say. Only my presence at work the next day would tell.

*   *   *

Climbing the red, carpeted stairs of the hotel, like every morning, I walked into the second-floor conference room when everyone else was. I sat next to Candice and Gretchen, who I didn't tell about the incident last night. Only a few minutes later did the parade of inspectors and managers made their way in, handing out room assignment lists like they were Tootsie Pops. One of the lists was mine. I was still employed.

I'd be cleaning the usual number of rooms today, roughly eleven on my list, out in the cabins, split fairly evenly between rooms I'd need to clean fully and those that were occupied. We'd been receiving a lot of help from the exchange students, too, so I knew today would be a manageable day.

By five-fifteen, most everyone was inside the cabin office restocking and organizing their carts for the next day, except for Tyler and me, who were collecting linen bags along the curbs of the road to help the Linen Truck Drivers, or LTDs. They'd been coming later while we'd been finishing earlier, so doing this for them made their job go more quickly. However, I also believed the managers just wanted to keep us busy, particularly Danica and Mary, the two assistant managers.

Our job was to throw all the blue and white bags of sheets and towels into one of the rattling wooden mule carts as we hauled it up and down the excruciatingly long hill. We would be taking care of the 500s while two other RAs did the 600s. I'd climbed this hill many times, carrying a vacuum, bags of dirty laundry, and three bins of supplies behind me. On days when the weather was anything but sunny, getting to the cabins at the top of the hill was that much more difficult.

Once we'd collected the bags, Tyler and I went all the way back up to the top with the empty cart to check for any stray bags we might have missed. It was when we were on top of the hill again, by cabin 508, that Tyler surprised me by telling me to get inside the cart.

"What? What do you mean *get inside*?"

He gestured to his cart. "Get in. I'll push you down the hill."

"You'll push me down the hill?" I repeated.

"Yes."

"Why?"

"Because it'll be fun. Just trust me," he said, a little exasperated.

I looked from him to the cart. Then from the cart to the bottom of the hill we were on. "But what if I crash or fall out?" I reasoned. "This thing balances on *two wheels*, Tyler."

"Lauren, I'll be pushing you the whole way down," he said. "I promise I won't let go."

At the risk of annoying him further with my endless safety questions, I took a deep breath in. "Okay," I said, pushing my nerves down. "Seriously, though, you better not let go." Then I stepped inside while he held the two handles, keeping the cart balanced.

"I won't," he smiled, satisfied with my answer.

My heart pounded as I waited for the moment he'd start to run down the hill, my knees scrunched up to my chest and fingers clenching the wooden sides of the wagon.

"Ready?" he said.

"I guess so."

"Here we gooo!" he called out, immediately thrusting the cart out in front of him and racing down the hill. What felt like a force of two G's disoriented me for a few seconds before I gathered myself enough to feel the blast of warm summer wind flying across my face. My messy bun, which was already falling off the side of my head, loosened to a floppy, crumpled ponytail. It wasn't long before my fear turned to thrill and I found myself grinning like a kid, relishing the adrenaline rush. Tyler let out a scream of exhilaration and I did the same, ignoring the attention of some of the nearby guests walking around their cabins.

About halfway down the hill, I suddenly realized just how fast we were approaching the LTD's large plastic laundry bins by the docking station of the cabin office at the bottom of the hill. I felt panic rising in my chest as I realized just how fast we were going without any indication of slowing down.

"Tyler!" I shouted over the rush of the wind. "Tyler, watch out!"

Seconds before crashing into them, he yanked back the cart back in an attempt to slow it down before swerving out of the way, just barely missing the large plastic bins. As he dodged them, he lost his grip and left me to coast to a stop for the last remaining seconds, the handles dropping to the ground behind me with a hard slap. My body jolted back, but I managed to keep myself upright enough to avoid rolling out of the cart or hitting my head on the pavement. When the cart scraped to a stop, I scrambled out and looked up to see a few people coming out of the cabin to see what all the noise was about, some grinning, others with concerned faces. Glancing back at Tyler, who was about ten feet behind me, I saw him bent over laughing and catching his breath.

"You said you weren't going to let go!" I yelled at him, letting some edge come into my voice.

"Oh my god, that was hilarious!" he cackled, his wavy red hair swishing back and forth with every laugh.

I pulled the elastic band out of my hair and proceeded to redo my messy bun. "Jesus Christ, Tyler," I said, twisting my hair back into its usual place.

He walked over to me and grabbed the cart when he composed himself. "You had to admit it was fun though, right?"

I studied him with a hard look but was met with unwavering amusement. He refused to let me be irritated with him, and a small smile cracked at the corner of my mouth as I gave in to his child-like glee. "Okay," I admitted against my will. "Only a little."

He wheeled the cart back into its usual place, tipping it against the back wall of the cabin office and we walked in to restock our bins, something we hadn't done yet. Clyde, who was a large man, both in width and height, walked over from the computer in the back of the room where he was inputting numbers. He was my inspector for the day and had a habit of requesting last-minute jobs from us, whether it be giving extra towels to a guest, cleaning a forgotten bathroom, or helping another RA with a final room.

"Hey guys," he began, his deep voice booming across the cabin office, "610 had an overflowed toilet and I'll need a couple of volunteers to help clean it up. I'll be going up there to take a look at it to make sure we don't need to get the biohazard team involved."

The biohazard *team? How bad can it be?* I thought to myself as I stacked rolls of toilet paper inside my plastic bin.

No one said anything. Most of them kept on restocking their bins, avoiding eye contact with him. Finally, I heard Piper say next to me, "I'll do it."

"Okay, we got one person," Clyde said, keeping an eye on the rest of us, waiting for a second volunteer.

The only sounds that were made came from the ruffling and shuffling of pulling housekeeping supplies from the shelves. People worked silently next to each other, folding towels into their bins and counting tea packets.

I can't believe I'm about to do this, I said to myself.

"I'll go," I said at last, ending the agony.

"Great. Thanks, Lauren," Clyde said with a nod. "You guys'll need rubber gloves, goggles, masks, all the PPE we got. Go on ahead and make your way up there when you're done restocking and wait for me when you get there."

Grabbing all the personal protective equipment we could find, Piper and I walked up to cabin 610, which of course, happened to be at the very top of the hill I had just sailed down. I could feel the tall mop handles banging against the same spot on my leg, which made me more irritated than was necessary, because I'd nearly crashed into seven-foot-tall laundry bins and was now preparing to clean toxic waste without recognition or reward. "We're damn good people for doing this," I said aloud, attempting to convince myself of its truth.

Piper nodded, her Judy Garland face studying the asphalt we were walking on. "We really are. It makes me wonder just how bad the room is if we need goggles and masks. I mean, I know we're supposed to be wearing them anyway when we're cleaning, but it must be really bad if Clyde is recommending it."

I shook my head. "We better be getting paid extra for this. I know we won't, but I'm not risking my health for Terrego."

We approached the cabin and waited on the stairs until Clyde met us there, minutes later, with his clipboard and radio in hand.

"Hey, guys," he sang as if we weren't just about to walk into potentially the most toxic cabin in all of Yellowstone. He reached for the jingling bundle of keys on his hip before plugging a bronze key into the matching keyhole of the yellow wooden door.

The smell hit us like a train, even through our masks. It was so putrid we had to open all the doors and windows because the stench had been stifled inside the cabin for so many hours.

"The guests didn't tell us about this until a few hours after leaving," Clyde said, walking toward the bathroom inside. Management must've mentioned that to him before he requested volunteers. "Apparently one of the guests here was sick and tried to use the toilet after throwing up into it. Ended up getting pretty backed up and overflowed onto the floor."

Even through the soles of my shoes I could feel the receding carpet squish with every step I took. It reminded me of that childhood game I used to play where I would pretend the floor was lava, except now it was feces and vomit mixed with toilet water.

It would be a massive understatement to say I regretted volunteering.

Piper and I had barely spoken when Clyde continued on, revealing more and more about the cabin, like it was a classic story. For me, it was a nightmare that only got worse.

"Yeah, it's been sitting here for a while now. We called the biohazard team earlier to clean some of it up, but they had to leave to get more supplies. They should be coming back later, so in the meantime, we'll just be cleaning up around the edges a little."

It was moments like these that reminded that kindness itself could be a curse. *What are we doing here then?* I wondered. They *should be here, the specialists. Not us. What if we get sick?*

"Hang on, guys. I'm gonna radio Claire to get more info before we get started," he said, stepping outside to radio management and probably a deep breath of fresh air.

Piper and I stayed inside, left to strategize how to tackle this monstrosity of a room.

"Are you seeing this?" I asked, studying the rest of the room.

"This is *bad*," she agreed.

"How the hell are we supposed to clean this? We have a mop and plastic gloves," I said, motioning to the bucket of cleaning supplies on the ground next to us. "I mean, what if we get pinkeye or something?"

She shrugged. "Management would probably still make us work and then throw a pizza party to say sorry."

"And to distract us from retaliation," I added, adjusting my mask.

I paused for a while, thinking about our next steps. "Should we...I don't know; should we just start with the bathroom then?"

She shrugged again, just as clueless as me. "I guess so. I'll start unclogging the toilet if you wanna start mopping the floor," she suggested.

Clyde returned a few minutes later, when we had only just begun cleaning, and told us to put a halt on it. "So it looks like the biohazard team is gonna be coming by to take care of all this. Are your guys' carts restocked?"

We nodded, mop and plunger in hand.

"You guys can head back to the hotel then. I'll sign your lists before you go."

We were out of that room faster than a five-legged greyhound.

CHAPTER 13

─────── ···◆◆◆··· ───────

We decided to spend the Fourth of July camping in Grand Teton National Park, just two and a half hours south of Yellowstone. Gretchen and I worked for most of the day, but Tyler and Dorian didn't, so they were in charge of grabbing a campsite.

Around four p.m. we met up at a brewery in town for an early dinner, then headed over to the middle of the town square for a fireworks show. Jackson Hole was a major tourist attraction in the Tetons, especially in the winter when it transitioned to a skiing resort. It was filled with shops, parks, restaurants, and quaint little sidewalks. The entrance of the park we were at was famous for being an arch constructed entirely of antlers—hundreds of them. It formed a rounded collection of what looked like thick, white thorns with a simple little sign hanging from it that read, "Jackson Hole, WY." All four of us would sit in that park on a blanket of grass, waiting for the night to fall and the fireworks to rise.

It was a perfect evening: a deep, pensive blue streaked with thin accents of purple. The wind was light, and my sweatshirt kept me just warm enough. It smelled fresh everywhere. I could smell the faint scent of wildflowers mixed with pine. Pine was inescapable; it followed you everywhere from Wyoming to Montana to Idaho, mixed with red cedar, firs, ash, and so many other varieties.

Dorian and Gretchen were next to me, absorbed in their own conversation. It became increasingly difficult to distinguish their dark features from the fall of the night, deep walnet curls, eyes, and lashes.

Tyler sat on my other side. We'd been making light conversation about nothing in particular. His features were a little easier to see at this time in the evening, particularly his red hair and paler skin.

"So what's the plan for the remainder of the night?" I asked, leaning back and crossing my legs, which were outstretched across the grass in front of me.

"Watch the fireworks, head back to camp, then get lit," he said, doing the same.

"Get lit?" I repeated, chuckling.

"Yeah. We bought two cases of beer, a couple bottles of huckleberry wine, and Jack Daniel's."

My eyes bulged out of my head. "*Jeez!* How much did you guys think we were gonna drink tonight? We can't go through all of that!"

"Not with that attitude," he joked dryly. "And don't worry, management's not here to catch us either."

"Right. What are the odds they're gonna be at that exact campsite at the exact same time? Which reminds me," I added, "I'm gonna be getting up early to head back in the morning."

He gave me a funny look. "You're gonna head back at the ass crack of dawn *tomorrow?*"

I shrugged. "Yeah, I gotta work."

Tyler eyed me, studying my face, which was genuine and unmoving. "Well, good luck with that. If I were you, I'd call in tomorrow and tell 'em you're sick or some shit."

"Who's sick?" Dorian asked, leaning in.

Tyler gestured to me. "She said they're heading back to Lake early tomorrow morning for work."

"Not Gretchen, just me," I corrected. "I'm borrowing her car tomorrow and she figured she'd just hitch a ride with you guys later."

Now it was Dorian's turn to eye me. "Dude. You're gonna be *wiped* tomorrow."

"Yeah, I know."

"Why not just call in sick?" he asked, repeating Tyler's thought.

"You know, Lauren, that wouldn't be a bad idea." Gretchen was looking over at me from behind Dorian. "You haven't even taken a day off work yet, have you? So you could probably afford to do it."

I weighed my options. She wasn't wrong. If I left, I would not only feel like a total vibe kill, but I'd also feel guilty about putting extra, last-minute work on both management *and* possibly another room attendant. At the same time, though, I knew they could afford it because we had more RAs than we ever did before.

"I'll think about it," I finally said.

They all nodded.

"You should do it," said Dorian.

"I don't know what I'd say. I suck at lying."

"Tell 'em something gross so they won't ask about it," said Tyler.

I thought about this for a few seconds. "I could tell them I have really bad period pains. That's something that actually happens to people."

They all shrugged, nodding in agreement.

The tricky part would just be waking up early enough to do it and praying I'd have enough cell service to make it happen at all. I could feel a small knot of anxiety forming in the pit of my stomach—not about making the call but about being caught. What would happen then? Would I get fired for real this time?

I caught myself spiraling and willed my ruminations to stop. *You are not the first person to call in fake-sick*, I reasoned. *You're one of the best housekeepers here. People with worse quality of work call in sick and still have their jobs.*

Dropping whatever tension had been building in my stomach, I instead chose to focus on what was in front of me: friends, mountains, and a break.

The first firework shot up from somewhere beyond the horizon of shops and bars, sending sparks of red and gold across the indigo sky. Next was orange, then blue, then green, all various shapes, sounds, and sizes. For the next half hour, I watched in admiration as a show of sparkling colors crackled across the sky, doing my best to push my aprehension aside.

*   *   *

Gretchen and I followed the guys in Dorian's Honda Accord across a dusty, bumpy road on the outskirts of Jackson Hole toward the campsite they managed to grab. The other sites were spread out far enough that you couldn't see or hear anyone unless they had a bonfire lit. Tufts of tumbleweeds were sprinkled across the ground in dry patches.

The first thing we did when we pulled in was get the fire going. Once it caught, we all huddled around it on long logs of wood cracking open beers and wine bottles. This was my second time drinking underage. In a strange way, it made me feel a part of something I was never able to relate to: rebellion. Nothing crazy, just simple adolescent rebellion.

Halfway through my bottle, I began to feel funny in my head and got the sensation that my brain was lagging about two seconds behind my words, giving me a particularly odd feeling of surrealism. I guess I must have said this out loud because Tyler got on a tangent, trying to convince me that I was not, in fact, drunk off less than one beer.

"Well, I sure as hell don't feel normal!" I cried back.

Tyler took a swig from the Jack Daniel's bottle he'd been holding for most of the night. I could see the bronze liquid glistening in the glow of the fire. "But that's how you're supposed to feel!" he said. "You're not supposed to feel normal when you drink!"

"You're confusing me. You know, I'm pretty sure it's the altitude," I reasoned. "Maybe my body just hasn't acclimated all the way yet."

I was recalling a fact I'd heard once: higher altitudes affect your red blood cells, which help with getting oxygen to various parts of your body. So if someone is a lightweight, like me, that meant I was at greater risk of getting drunk more quickly. Plus, it'd been hours since I last ate, so there was that.

"You don't get drunk off altitude!" Tyler shouted again, stumbling through his words and over his feet as he got up to change seats.

I shook my head, tired of bantering with him. "That's... not what I meant." Thinking of Gretchen, I turned to her, hoping she would validate my experience. She was laughing over something—what that was I had no idea. "Gretchen! Do you feel anything?"

"What?" she giggled to herself. "I don't know!"

I then turned to Dorian. "Don't *you* feel anything?"

I noticed he was already looking at me. "No, not really."

"Really?"

"Really."

"Huh," I thought aloud before pausing in thought. Then I asked, "Dorian, how'd you get your name?"

He gave a bit of a sigh, indicating this wasn't the first time he'd been asked. "Well," he started, shifting around on the tree log he was sitting on, "my dad read a lot of Oscar Wilde right before I was born and decided to name me after a character in *The Picture of Dorian Gray*."

I said, "Oh. Well, that's kinda cool, being named after a book. I was named after a billboard."

His face twisted in a mix of confusion and amusement. "You were what?"

I took a deep breath in, gathering myself. "My dad said he was driving home from work one day and saw an ad for Ralph Lauren cologne. I guess he made a mental note of it because when he got home, he told my mom about it and she must've liked it too. That's how I was named after a billboard."

Everyone just kind of stared at me until Tyler suddenly shouted, pointing across the way to something unidentifiable. "Hey, that's Derrick from the EDR! I'm gonna go say hi to him."

We all looked over at the lightly illuminated campsite on the other side of the tumbleweed field in front of us. They also had a fire. It looked like there were twice as many people and, frankly, that didn't appeal to me at all.

"Tyler, you can't even walk straight," said Dorian.

"But what if they have s'mores?" he cried.

"If they've got s'mores, I want some!" Gretchen yelled.

She and Tyler hobbled across the field toward the site— Gretchen mostly guiding him, whose feet couldn't help but change direction with every step. Only Dorian and I remained, sitting in silence across the fire from each other. It crackled and popped between us, filling the air with burning birch.

"You wanna know something?" I finally said, "You play it like you're cool and tough, but I think you're secretly a big softie."

Dorian, it seemed, was attempting to figure out what to do with that insight. He just sort of stared at me with his tired, dark eyes for a second before resting them on the red, flickering flames in front of him. He looked like he was caught, targeted...*seen*, and he wasn't sure what to do about it. His thick dark brows were knitted together in thought. He eventually looked over at me, vulnerable and timid.

"Just don't tell anyone, okay?"

I smiled. "I won't."

The quiet of the night filled the air around us. No cars whizzing by, no sirens in the distance, not even crickets, just the crackling and popping of the flames and distant conversation from campsites beyond ours.

"Tell me something not many people know about you," I said.

Dorian's eyes flickered up, unprepared for another question of mine. "What's something not many people know about me...?" he repeated to himself. His thick brows knitted together again as he thought about his answer. "Well...I used to like Katy Perry," he finally admitted.

"Really?" I beamed, delighted with the honesty of his answer.

"Yeah. I don't listen to her anymore, though."

"Why not?" I asked.

"I don't know," he said, dropping his gaze to what must have been his shoes before looking back up. "I guess because it's not manly."

I paused, then repeated his words back, one at a time, to make sure I understood them. "You don't listen to Katy Perry because you don't think it's manly...."

He didn't say anything.

"Well, so what?" I asserted after another moment. "You're allowed to like her music. You can listen to whomever you want!"

He half-smiled, then looked up at me with something new in his face. Almost like relief. "Thanks."

I took a swig of my remaining beer that had been sitting on the ground near the end of the log I was sitting on. Normally, I would bounce my leg up and down or pull my hands up into my shirt sleeves, but instead, I sat still, staring at the fire again and sipping my beer.

"So if you had a million dollars, what would you do with it?" I asked again, barely looking up from the flames.

"Mm," he thought, more sure of himself this time. "Probably just keep traveling. Hit up more national parks. I'm at twenty-nine right now, so I'd like to get up to Wrangell-St. Elias in Alaska. Mostly because of its size."

"How big is it?"

"Six times larger than Yellowstone."

My eyes must have been the size of bowling balls because Dorian just smiled to himself again, like he was proud of his answer.

"Dang! I don't even know how big that is!" I exclaimed.

He smiled. "Yeah, it's pretty huge. Trying to get in all the traveling I can do before I have to be a full-time adult."

"What, like job stuff?" I asked.

Dorian nodded. "Yeah. I'm going to school again when the summer's over."

I sat up, intrigued. "Really, for what? I thought you already graduated."

"I did. But I'm going to Sussex, England, for a study abroad opportunity, then applying to law school."

"Oh *shit*." I sat still, taken aback by the prestige of his answer. "So what does that look like?"

"Well, I take the LSAT in January, this entrance exam, and then start the application process right after. Hoping to get into UPenn or something."

"That's amazing!" I enthused. "Do you think you'll like it?"

Dorian shrugged again. "I think so. I just...wanna be happy, you know?"

I nodded. Even in my drunken state, I took him seriously. If there's anything I'd learned about being in Yellowstone, it was that everyone came here for something more, something beyond the mundane, the expected, the daily rigmarole, the conformity they were subjected to in their real lives. I packed my bags to find belonging, to myself and something beyond myself. Maybe he was doing the same.

I heard the echoes of Gretchen and Tyler's gabbing in the distance. Their silhouettes bobbed up and down through the thick of the tumbleweeds, Tyler's figure in particular, swaying this way and that with each little movement.

"We're baaaack!" Gretchen sang.

"They had s'mores!" Tyler screeched.

"Nice," I said.

Tyler stumbled over to sit on my extra-long log of wood, Jack Daniel's still in hand, which was somewhat impressive given his instability. He didn't quite make it and instead, nearly fell into the fire.

"*Whoa!*" everyone belted in unison, scrambling to catch him all at once.

"Why don't you give me the bottle for a while?" said Dorian, reaching for it.

Tyler gave his head a violent shake. "No, it's mine!" He then proceeded to run away from us, toward the main dirt road we came in on. It wouldn't have been a big deal if it were daytime since hardly any cars came down that road, but because it *was* so dark, we risked losing him among the tumbleweeds. It took a three-person effort to corral him back to his spot on the log next to me, where he slumped to the floor to barf, nearly rolling himself into it. Dorian eventually took him into his tent thirty minutes later to strip him of his puke-stained clothes after he passed out.

The rest of us stayed up until three in the morning. The fire had hardly dimmed since its construction four hours before, and none of us quite felt like retiring to our tents. That's when

I got an idea. I stood up and walked over to Gretchen's and my tent to pull out my air mattress, then sleeping bag, and dragged it over to a spot near the campfire.

"What are you doing?" asked Dorian.

"Sleeping outside," I answered.

"Why?"

"Because I can."

They both paused to consider this, looking like they were doing math in their heads.

"Fuck it," said Dorian, getting up to pull his sleeping bag out of his and Tyler's tent. "I think that's a great idea."

"Me too," added Gretchen, standing up to revisit the tent for hers.

"I don't think I've ever done this before," said Dorian, balling his up under his arm before planting it approximately three feet from the burning coals of the firepit.

"Me neither," Gretchen agreed, poking her head inside the nylon walls of the tent before pulling hers out next.

"I always thought it would be so cool to do something like this," I admitted. "No time like the present, right?"

The remainder of our late night was filled with lazy chatter until, one by one, each of us succumbed to the invisible weight of fatigue. And that's how we slept—exposed to the elements, under the subtle glow of the Milky Way, with the grandeur of the Tetons, and by the radiating heat of a crackling fire.

*   *   *

I got just two hours of sleep that night. I was awake by five-thirty, preparing for a phone call, albeit a slightly intoxicated one, to the Lake housekeeping office to explain my incoming absence. My fingers reached out for my phone that I felt slide to the ground earlier. The rubber Otterbox cover felt gritty and dusty from falling on the powdery floor as I picked it up. Squinting one eye open, I checked to see if there was enough reception to even make the call and, to my surprise, there was.

Squirming up to the top of my bag, like a caterpillar to the tip of a leaf, I felt the sharp, crisp bite of the morning air, persuading me to crawl back into my meshy cocoon. It was much lighter than I expected it to be at this hour. A pink halo glowed from behind the backdrop of the mountain range, signaling the start of the day. I push myself up on my elbows to look around, admiring it all. Dorian and Gretchen, on either side of me, were still asleep.

My hair, usually long and straight, had twisted and curled into various tangled directions as I attempted to run a lazy hand through it. Instead, I just shoved it all over to one side of my head to get it out of my face. I didn't recall bringing a jacket or something heavier than a sweatshirt to wear, so I braced myself for the cool, dewy atmosphere by crossing my arms and stuffing my hands into my armpits.

I walked toward our two cars parked nearby, Gretchen's Jeep and Dorian's Accord, passing thick clusters of tumbleweeds along the way. My stomach began to grow anxious as I rehearsed the script I'd planned in my head yesterday evening. Praying Gretchen's car was unlocked, I tried the driver's-side door, and, to my delight, it opened. I hoisted myself into the driver's seat, leaving the door open and my left foot to dangle outside the frame.

I typed in my phone's passcode before pulling up the dial icon on the screen. Nine circular buttons glowed back at me, waiting to be pressed. My fingers quivered as they dialed, one at a time, the number I had saved to the notes app of my phone: *307-555-4052*.

The electronic ringing tone sounded through my phone and my stomach grew more and more tense. Despite the early hour, I half-expected someone to answer, maybe Mary or Danica. It didn't seem like they had lives at all outside of the housekeeping office. Instead, to my relief, it rang all the way through to the end where I was prompted to leave a message.

"Hey, this is Lauren Erickson," I said, allowing the grogginess of my voice to come through. "Wanted to let you know that I've been awake all night with a really awful case of period cramps that I can't seem to shake. Took some meds for them, but I'm not sure I'll be well enough to come to work today. I should be good to go tomorrow, though, but wanted to let you know as soon as possible so you'd have enough time to make any changes to today's list assignments. Thank you and let me know if there's anything else I need to do."

Click. I ended the call.

I took a deep breath in, allowing all the tension in my stomach to be exhaled into the world, away from me. Then I closed my eyes, willing my body to become still and grounded before leaving the car. After a few more breaths, I opened them slowly and stepped out, planting my feet one at a time onto the solid ground, kicking up a minuscule cloud of dust. I clicked the door shut and walked around to the other side of the car where I came face-to-face with the Grand Teton mountain range.

All around its jagged edges, the soft colors of morning began to take full bloom. The pink glow from just a minute ago had now melted into various shades of lavender and cyan, swirling around the tips of the peaks. The morning sun, barely peeking across the horizon, sent a warm, cascading glow across the ice caps and the wildflower-covered prairie land below. I could only stand and stare.

Moments like these were only ever meant to be observed and felt. Mother Nature sure had a way of knowing Her own beauty; She never needed someone to say She was beautiful in the first place because She always believed it. Our job, as Her inhabitants, was to recognize it when we saw it and let it all in once we did. We were never to pocket it for ourselves, take credit for Her grandeur, or strip Her of Her qualities for something more profitable. True beauty had no agenda and only ever knew how to be itself.

I turned around after a few more minutes to walk back to the warmth of my sleeping bag. It was nearly six a.m. Dorian and Gretchen were still slumbering in theirs, unmoved, with the remaining bits of coal still smoking in the firepit. Everything smelled earthy and real. Nothing had changed or moved. My eyelids became heavy while my fingers wilted into their natural positions, only feeling the cold breath of the morning on my cheeks.

CHAPTER 14

––––––––– ··•◆•◆•·· –––––––––

I got a tattoo.

It was an early birthday present I gave myself; I wanted to do something with a few of my friends before they began to head home again. August would be here in a couple of weeks, so I knew my days with them were limited. No one believed I would go through with it, but I was a woman of my word.

The design was a simple outline of a mountain range with a circle, representing the sun, in the middle of it. It ran along the inner arch of my right foot to account for all the miles I'd walked this summer: between the housekeeping, hiking, walking, commuting, and even the herculean effort it took to physically *bring* myself to the park, my feet were the ones that carried me. Through all my Yellowstone experience, and even before then, they never failed me. Never broke, got sprained, got twisted, or anything. They were my most reliable mode of transportation.

We spent the whole afternoon wandering around Bozeman, a fun little college town about three hours north. It wasn't just my birthday we were celebrating, though—it was also Tyler's and Sarah's. Hers was at the end of the month and Tyler's was at the beginning of August. The tattoo was my own idea.

No one else did it. They just watched with amusement the various ways my face contorted as the artist kept going over the boniest part of my foot.

For some reason, though, I kept getting the impression that something was up with Tyler. He hadn't really spoken to me for a while, and I didn't know what the problem was. The only thing that got him talking was seeing me walk around with a bandaged foot in Bozeman and the dance that would be happening later today at the Lake Lodge. Everyone had been talking about it for weeks, particularly the plan for pregaming.

We'd be meeting in Dorian's room with his roommate, the bartender who served us the drinks in the sunroom no too long ago. Because the theme was western, I wore a flannel top with jeans. I even wore makeup for the first time in three months. Feeling a little self-conscious, both about the dance and my makeup skills, I walked out of Pelican, down the flight of rickety wooden stairs, across the parking lot, and across the street toward Osprey, where Dorian lived.

I knocked on the door a couple of times, even though it was left slightly ajar.

"Hey, what's goin' on?" he greeted, flinging it wide open.

Five or six other people were already inside, mostly people from the housekeeping crew, including Tyler.

Bottles of liquor, wine, and beer decorated the dresser in a variety of labels and colors. I began to feel a little out of my element as my nerves swam around inside me, making me feel a bit warm in my flannel.

"What can I getcha?" Dorian's roommate chimed.

"I'll have a beer," I said.

"What kind?"

"What kind?"

He nodded. "Yeah, what kind? We've got IPA, lager, cider, ale…"

"Uh, ale, I guess." I wasn't totally confident that I chose something I would actually enjoy, and I was correct. The dark brown bottle I received tasted much fuller and denser, and weirdly, a little sweet.

"Good?"

"Mhm," I lied as I took another sip.

"Hey, is it me or is it hot in here?" someone asked, reading my mind. "Can we open a window or something?"

Dorian crossed the room to crack their only window open, releasing a cool rush of air into the room.

"So we're gonna play a game," Sam, one of the housekeeping inspectors I sometimes worked with said, announced in her sandpapery voice. Everyone started ooh-ing to each other and wiggling their eyebrows at this. I just stood quietly next to the door, not entirely sure of what I was doing here in the first place. I was afraid of what she had to say next.

She continued, "One person asks a question and flips a coin, and while the coin is in the air, you decide if it's going to be heads or tails. If you're right, you don't have to answer it. If you're wrong, you do."

Sam pulled a quarter out from her back pocket and looked at Tyler, who was piled on one of the twin mattress nearby with four others. "Here's an example. Tyler," she said, "how many people have you slept with?"

Everyone giggled and gasped in disbelief at her question. She flipped the coin, he called tails, and it landed on exactly that: tails. Sam clicked her tongue. "All right, you dodged that one."

Relief flooded his face. They went on like this for twenty minutes, the questions becoming increasingly more and more risqué, something I was more than uncomfortable with.

Suddenly, I was handed the quarter and was put on the spot to ask something. Everyone watched me with expectancy, waiting for a saucy question that would never come. "Tyler," I said slowly, attempting to think of something decent in the few seconds I had. "Would you rather…pee lightning or wipe with shards of glass?"

"What?" he asked, like it was the weirdest question he'd heard in his life. Everyone's faces twisted into a combination of confusion and amusement. I heard a couple of people giggle and whisper something to each other.

Clearly, that wasn't the right question to ask.

Faking a smile, I repeated the question, this time even more uncertain, "Would you rather pee lightning or wipe with shards of glass?" I flipped the coin, and he called tails. It landed on heads, so he had to answer.

Tyler glanced at everyone around the room as if he was looking for a way out. "Um, I don't know, I guess pee lightning?"

I handed off the coin as quickly as I could, like it was burning a hole in my hand. After that, I didn't say much or do much, sort of just wanting to crawl into a deep, dark hole and only emerge after everyone had left. I felt the same way I was now at birthday parties as a kid—left out, a step behind, not quite with it. There was something I just didn't understand here, a magic ingredient I didn't have. I wanted to be a part of it but couldn't. I was doing it wrong. I felt excluded.

They went for three more rounds before Dorian noticed what time it was: eight-thirty, roughly half an hour after they opened the doors. Buzzed and quiet, I followed behind, last in line, as they filed out down the hall and out the door. They knew a backway to the Lodge so we wouldn't have to walk down the main road. It came out right by the employee pub after taking a short path through the nearby woods where you would eventually see the large wooden cabin of a building. I listened to them talk and laugh with each other, not entirely sure what I was doing here with them.

Security officers acting as bouncers stood at the door of the Lodge's rec center where the party was being held, to check our IDs. I shouldn't have been surprised because the only thing Terrego really cracked down on was underage drinking, despite the number of people I know who did hard drugs out here, including two of the three managers. The only reason I knew that was because Dorian told me. So since I wasn't of drinking age yet, despite being just two weeks away from it, they gave me a little yellow wristband so I guess the people inside would know not to give me anything. Not that I was going to try anyway.

Because I was at the back of the line, I had completely lost track of everyone by the time I got inside. It was crowded, incredibly dark, and the strobe lights made it hard to see anything. Actually, the first thought I had was, *I'm back in high school.*

For my senior prom, I wanted to go all out. I wanted to be bold and brilliant, to wear something no one would expect of me. So, I ordered a crimson mermaid-style dress online, decorated in intricate red lace. I wanted to be *regal.* I got my hair done, wore bright lipstick, and allowed the shoulders of my dress to drape slightly off my shoulders, revealing the hard shape of my collarbone.

That night, I drove myself to the dance where I'd meet the rest of the girls and their dates there. It didn't bother me that I didn't have someone to take me to prom. In fact, I kind of liked driving myself.

Upon walking in, I felt eyes all over me. Chaperones, classmates, it seemed as though I'd captured the attention of almost everyone who was near that entrance. Part of me didn't know what to do with it, but the other part didn't mind so much because I'd planned for this. I knew I risked being seen dressing up in the way that I had, actually *seen*. And I was.

I managed to find everyone by the dance floor and sauntered my way over, feeling confident for the first time in a long time. I liked the way my dress swished around my ankles as I walked. All at once, we began dancing to "Shut Up and Dance" by Walk the Moon, jumping up and down, throwing our arms and hair around, giving ourselves away to the night. I felt light and free, like I might actually have fun.

By the time that song ended, I was ramped up and ready for the next. Instead, what played was "All of Me" by John Legend, a slow song. I watched partners pair off and significant others embrace each other as the mood light changed from strobe lights to purples and pinks.

"Don't worry, Lauren! We'll get the next song together!" my friend shouted as she locked hands with her boyfriend, turning away to walk farther into the crowd.

Disappointed, I walked off to one of the nearby tables that sat in the shadow of the room, away from all the lights and glamour. I left my phone in the bag that I'd checked when I initially walked in, so all I could do was sit and watch couples dance. Against my will, watching them made me feel hurt and bitter inside. But I couldn't look away.

Suddenly, a guy I'd known since kindergarten came over and sat next to me. He was nice, but, unfortunately, I remembered him as being the smelly kid in school. He wasn't that way anymore, but olfactory senses make it difficult for you to forget a memory like that.

"Hey, Lauren," he said.

"Hey, Aaron," I greeted. "How's it goin'?"

He shrugged. "Eh, okay. You enjoying the dance?"

I shrugged back. "It's okay."

"Yeah. Hey, you look nice tonight."

I nodded with my eyes on the floor, praying he wouldn't ask me to dance. I wasn't in the mood, and I didn't want to be looked at anymore. "Thank you."

I think part of him knew that. Instead, he just sat there with me, giving me someone to talk to while I watched everyone else dance, which was all I really needed.

When the song ended, I stood up, expecting my friend to come out from the crowds to pull me in to dance with her, but she didn't. The next began to play and I stood there for thirty seconds, looking for her, trying at every angle to find anything that might identify her. She never emerged though. I could feel hot tears pooling at the base of my eyes. As stupid as it felt, it bothered me that she promised to dance with me and didn't make an effort to find me. I trusted her to include me tonight, and I was beginning to feel the opposite.

"Hey, I'm gonna run off to the bathroom really quick," I said, avoiding eye contact with Aaron. "I'll see you later."

"See ya," he waved.

I *click-clocked* my way in heels across the dance floor over to the bagging area where I requested my purse. Clutching it, I fished my phone out and strode over to the bathrooms on the other side, where, luckily, hardly any ladies were.

I tucked myself into a corner of the restroom where I unlocked my phone and called my mom. Thankfully, she picked up after the first couple of rings.

"Hey, girl! How's prom so far?" she sang.

I sniffled, trying not to sound like I was on the verge of crying. "Would it be lame if I came home right now?"

"Why? What's wrong?"

I squeezed my eyes shut and let the first tear inevitably fall, ignoring the looks from the two other girls in the bathroom. My voice gave in, and I could only manage to whisper the next words. "I'm not having fun."

Her voice dropped into something much more sympathetic. "Oh, baby, I'm sorry. You know what? No, it's not lame. Come on over and we'll get comfy and eat Ben & Jerry's. That sound good?"

I nodded, even though I knew she couldn't see it. "I'll be home in twenty."

Walking into the rec center of the Lodge this time, I didn't even try. I knew the feeling well. Instead, I sat in one of those chairs along the wall, for sad loners like me. I knew I didn't belong there, but I sat anyway.

What hurt the most, though, wasn't sitting alone. It was that sad voice of the blue girl in the back of my head that pointed out the simple fact: *No one is looking for you.*

I'd had enough, so I got up and left.

Again.

Avoiding eye contact with the security guards, I rushed through the double doors and shielded my face from the mingling guests on the porch. Stepping down the few stairs and out the driveway, my feet took an immediate right out onto the main road on the long way back toward the dorms. That same mascara-stained tear rolled down my cheek almost exactly the way it had at prom and at that bar in college. I was older now, wiser, stronger, yet I continued to repeat this pattern of crying and carrying myself home in the dark. I felt pathetic and angry, yet more confused than ever.

Why does this keep happening to me? I thought. *What is it that I'm missing?*

I was only a couple hundred feet down the road when something compelled me to look up. The Milky Way Galaxy spilled across the sky in its entirety. It was like some divine source had put a celestial crack in the sky, and just beyond that was a world I'd always dreamed of belonging to, just beyond the stars and the thin sliver of moon.

I was so lonely at that moment that I walked into that field and sat on a rock to look at it some more, just so it felt like I had something else to sit with. Then all the tears came out of me the same way water leaves a wet sponge when you squeeze it. The snot, the lurching, the jagged breathing, it all came, and I didn't even try to keep it all in. If I wouldn't even let myself cry in an empty field, then where else could I do it?

I felt like a flamingo in a flock of pigeons, knowing I stuck out but not understanding why. I wanted to be gray. Boring, gray, and normal. Though because I couldn't change that about myself, I instead learned to leave where I didn't belong. Leaving, for me, was an act of self-respect. That's why I left prom. That's why I left that bar in college. That's why I left the Lodge. *Because it wasn't fun.*

The skin under my eyes was sticky now as the flood of tears began to dry themselves. I looked up to the sky again, admiring all the constellations I wished I knew. Each one glimmered with a silvery brightness that I imagined as a million little winks just for me.

I suddenly felt my phone vibrate. On my screen was a text notification from Tyler: *Where r u?*

I looked away. It took them twenty minutes to recognize my absence. Part of me was relieved, but the other part was angry and wanted to stay that way. Instead, I picked it up and replied with one word: *Outside.*

My phone buzzed again a minute later. *Where?*

I looked up to the sky again, this time mostly for something to stare at while I thought about everything: my state, my options, my life. I wanted to know what to do next. Let's say they want me to come back inside, and let's say I do. What if I don't have a good time? Then that would hurt twice as much and continue to confirm any detestation I had toward parties and social gatherings at all. I wanted to have fun and do normal young adult things, but each time I tried, I was met with neglect.

I continued to look up when, suddenly, a shooting star streaked across the black sky, a big bright one. I watched it, surprised and in awe, as it shot across the stratosphere like a golden-white tear through a piece of sparkling, indigo paper.

It was the first shooting star I'd ever seen in my life, and the fact that I was the only one who saw it made me feel...I don't know, *special.* I had to believe it was for me. I needed to.

I took it as a sign to try one more time. I picked up my phone from the dusty ground and texted, *Coming back.* My arms and legs, weak with catharsis, hoisted me as best they could off the rock. My feet then guided me back to the Lodge as I wiped all evidence of crying from my face.

Walking back into the glowing light of the Lodge's porch made me feel nervous again, like I was walking back into the lion's den. Shielding my face from the stray bodies hanging around on the deck, I darted back into the black, strobe-lit cave of the Lodge.

I didn't see anyone by the doors when I returned, so I chose to lean against the wall and look from there before putting all my energy and attention into scouring the dance floor. Then out of the blue, a rough hand yanked me by my wrist out into the crowd. Initially offended and confused, I soon noticed it was Tyler and relaxed. He had a big, sweaty smile on his face. He dragged me over to the rest of the group without saying a word, just dancing like mad.

Everyone gave wide smiles when I was reintroduced. I was bobbing up and down to the music, feeling awkward and unsure, until a song I knew came on: "Sweet Caroline" by Neil Diamond. I couldn't help but give in to it. I started singing and dancing with everyone else to it—it was hard not to. Eventually, I became another sweaty member of the crowd. I bounced and twirled with everyone there until two a.m. when "You Got a Friend in Me" by Randy Newman came on and Tyler asked me to dance—another first.

He shifted me into what felt like a ballroom-dancing position. My left hand rested on his shoulder while his hand held up my right and we baltered around the room together until it was over. What I appreciated most about that moment was that he didn't try anything. He didn't try to kiss me or move his hands around or anything. All he did was dance with me, and that's exactly what I needed.

When it was over, I felt happy. Relieved. Thankful. Tonight had changed something for me, whether it was fate, destiny, or even just a plain old break in the repeating pattern of my social life. I needed it.

Walking back through the woods with everyone, I finally felt included. *Finally*. Tyler and I hung toward the back of the group, talking and joking like old friends, bypassing whatever awkwardness there had been between us.

"So why did you leave?" he asked.

"'Cause I've never liked dances," I admitted.

Even in the dark, I could see his puzzled face. "Really? But you've been asked out to dances in school, right?"

I shook my head. "No."

He stopped in his tracks. "Wait. You've never gotten asked out to a single dance? Ever?"

"No," I said again.

He started walking again, quiet in thought. Then he spoke. "Not to sound cheesy or anything, but I'm really proud of you for coming back."

I smiled. "Me too."

CHAPTER 15

····◆·◆··

Sarah was leaving today. We were standing by the parking lot together where we first drove in on our arrival in Yellowstone. It was a bittersweet moment for me. She was the first friend I'd made out there, the first person I got a Fishing Bridge milkshake with, the first person I'd gone on an overnight hike with, even if it did end up being a pain in the ass between the mosquitoes and Frank's misogyny. I could almost laugh about it now.

"I'm going to miss you so much," she said, hugging me.

"I'm going to miss you, too," I answered, squeezing her back. "I'll be right behind you just two weeks from now."

"Keep me updated with things! I hope you have a great birthday party with Candice and Tyler, too. I'm sorry I won't be able to make it." She smiled in that kind, charming way of hers.

"Don't even worry about it. And I will! I'm supposed to work the next day, too, so that'll be interesting. Text me when you get home, okay?"

Her drive would be much shorter than mine, since she lived just over in Idaho. We exchanged addresses, so we could write to each other like real pen pals instead of texting like regular people. There was something nice about receiving letters. She could send me cute little watercolor pictures and I could send her sketches around the margins of my notes to her.

From the sidewalk, I watched her get into her car, start the engine, and drive off, giving me a giant wave from inside as she made her way down the driveway to the main road that looped around Lake.

Normally, I wouldn't know what to do with myself after being roommate-less. She was my go-to person for all local hikes, walks, or general store snack runs. Lately, though, I'd found myself spending a little more time than usual with Piper since the toxic nightmare of cabin 610 a couple of weeks ago. She mentioned her sister would be coming in later today and was planning on hitting up the gym until leaving for the Bozeman airport to get her. She and I made plans to meet up there sometime after Sarah left.

"Hey," she said when I walked into the rec center that had been a party house just a few days before. She was on the elliptical and was the only person there.

"Hey," I said back, walking over to the nearby rack of basketballs to bounce around. I was never much of a traditional athlete—basketball, volleyball, softball, none of those sports were ever my thing. I preferred to enjoy myself casually by shooting hoops and walking around bouncing a ball for fun.

"Where is everyone?" I asked over the loud slap of the basketball echoing throughout the wood-paneled gymnasium.

"They're all out hammocking," she said, referring to the friend group.

"No, I mean, I thought the gym would be pretty active for this time of day," I clarified. It didn't bother me that they were out together. I was wanting a bit of a break from the group anyway.

"Oh. I don't know, maybe the weather just isn't motivating enough for them or something," Piper said. I turned to look out the wall of windows behind the basketball hoop at the heavy, gray clouds rolling in. I could smell the storm from here, thick and damp.

I turned around. "Didn't everyone know it was supposed to rain this afternoon? Why'd they go out hammocking?" I asked.

She shrugged, her face pink with perspiration and effort. "Beats me. Maybe they wanted to squeeze it in before being cooped up inside."

I nodded, returning to my basketball when I heard one of the metal doors open. Glancing over, I saw it was Tyler, which was a surprise. I let the ball bounce back up, then caught it and held it under my arm.

"Hey," I said. "I thought you were out hammocking with everyone else."

He shook his head. "Nah, left early. Clouds were rolling in, so I bailed." Noticing the basketball I had tucked under my arm, he motioned toward it. "Wanna play one-on-one?"

I laughed. "I'm not very good. I'm mostly just doing this for fun."

Tyler smiled back in response. "It's easy. All you're doing is just trying to stop me from making a shot."

I rolled my eyes. "I mean, I know that much."

"So, let's play," he said, getting into that low, guarded position that basketball players do.

I half-heartedly agreed. It didn't take long for the two of us to start squeaking across the court and building up a mild sweat. Normally I find conventional sports boring when I'm watching and intimidating when I'm playing, but this time, it felt kind of fun. I was actually enjoying myself a little.

"Oh, shoot!" Piper suddenly exclaimed from across the room. "I'm late! Dang it, I told her I was going to be on time. Ugh! Oh, hey, Tyler," she said, casually addressing his presence before grabbing her stuff.

"See ya later," I said, waving to her even though her back was already to me as she sprinted toward the double doors before opening and closing them with a hard, metal *clang*.

It was just us now. I was starting to feel a bit tired and wanted to sit for a minute.

"I'm gonna go grab my water," I said, nodding to my black drawstring bag on the other side of the room. When I grabbed it, I turned to sit on the hard wooden floor. I looked past Tyler to the tall wall of windows again, noticing the first few drops of rain. Didn't take but a minute or two for it to turn into a complete downpour.

"Oh, boy," I sighed, staring at it all. "How're we gonna manage to get back with that?"

Tyler walked over to sit next to me, gesturing to my water bottle. I handed it to him to let him have a drink. He took one giant gulp before speaking. "No idea. Not gonna be fun though."

"Well," I pondered for a second before gathering my bag. "Might as well make a break for it."

"Oh, are we leaving?" Tyler looked surprised.

"Well, I don't know," I said, "waiting it out would take too long, don't you think?"

"Maybe," he said, before considering something that spread a devilish smile across his face. "Let's have a race."

I laughed again. "A race? That's not fair. I'm already tired! You'll win."

"We won't know unless we try though, right?"

I stared at him, hoping my glare would change his mind, but, unsurprisingly, it didn't. Instead, I threw my hands up in defeat. "Okay. Let's go."

We walked toward a singular wood-paneled back door, opposite the main double doors Piper ran out of. Upon opening it, I immediately felt the cool rush of a summer rainstorm blow past me and into the rec room behind me. Goosebumps popped up all over my arms.

I heard Tyler's voice next to me. "Ready...set...*go!*"

Bolting out that back door, I sprinted with him through the shortcut in the woods, my strong legs carrying me past walls of pines and my drawstring back bouncing against my bag with each step. I focused on my breathing and form, orienting myself for optimal performance. After all, running was my specialty. I instantly snapped back into my high school race days, my body charging forward with every technique it could remember—arms thrusting forward, never crisscrossing, breathing in my nose, out my mouth, feet pounding at one-eighty strides a minute to protect my shins and joints from impact.

Halfway through the path, though, my throat caught fire in a dry, sticky kind of way. My legs started to burn with lactic acid, growing more and more tired with every stride I took until I eventually slowed to a jog, then a stop. I was out of shape, my breath and legs heavy with fatigue.

Tyler was way ahead of me, still sprinting. Probably sensing something, he looked over his shoulder to see me hunched over, hands resting on my thighs as I gathered myself.

"What are you doing?" he shouted through the rain. I could just barely hear him.

"I'm tired!" I shouted back.

"C'mon!" he said, picking up his stride again, not even waiting for me.

I picked up my stride again, pushing through the burn and exhaustion, until I made it out of the woods and onto the familiar asphalt path by the dorms, at which point I slowed to a final stop. Tyler had stopped about twenty feet in front of me in the parking lot by Pelican. The rain had lightened enough to where I could see him more clearly, but it didn't take long for my goosebumps to return. The cool breeze flapped against my clothes, and I immediately wished for a scalding hot shower to unthaw the chilly layer of rain that had drenched my skin.

"You know, a girl who runs is something that gets a boy's attention," I heard him say.

Confused, I furrowed my eyebrows together. "What?" I walked closer to hear him better, noticing the way his usually bright, ginger hair draped wet across his forehead, browner and smokier now.

"Girls who run get my attention," he repeated, his penetratingly blue eyes watching me.

Suddenly feeling a little uncomfortable, I laughed, attempting to shake it off. "Are you making a pass at me?"

"Maybe I am," he half-smiled.

Mine vanished. "Oh."

He took a step toward me. "Is that okay?"

My eyes immediately dropped to the glossy black asphalt. My heart pounded again in my chest just as much as it had been a minute ago, running through the woods. I didn't want this. I didn't want to be seen by him. Tyler was a friend. He was a *friend*. I felt stupid, like it should've been obvious, like I should've seen it coming a mile away. He joked with me, he walked with me, he *danced* with me, he—

"What do you think about us?" Tyler asked me, taking another step forward.

I looked up, forcing myself to meet his gaze. "What do you mean?"

"I mean what do you think about us? About maybe being together?"

Something about this scared me. I wasn't ready for this conversation. I didn't want to think about him romantically. All I could manage to do was shake my head, eyes wide. "I-I don't know..."

"You don't have to if you don't want to," he said, his voice calm and even.

I didn't say anything.

"It would only be until we left," he added. "That's a little less than two weeks. Then after that, we can go our separate ways. We can just see how it goes and if things don't work out, we can split without any hard feelings."

The possibility of exclusivity brought thoughts to my mind that filled me with dread, something I wasn't yet ready for—a certain...shall we say, *expectation* I knew guys had of their girlfriends. I didn't want that. At the same time, though, he did say that we could always call it off if we wanted to. Maybe if I went through with this, I would know what to expect when someone special *did* come along. It could be like a practice run.

Arms shaking, I crossed them together in an attempt to brace myself against the rain and my nerves. "Okay," I agreed, somewhat reluctantly. "Sure."

His eyes brightened. "Really?"

I nodded, trying my best to seem genuine about it. Truthfully, though, I was scared. I didn't know what to expect. I'd hardly dated anyone before. I didn't know what to do, what to expect, how to act, how to be. I knew how to be looked at by guys, but never actually *seen* by them, and that's what scared me—the vulnerability.

I pushed my reserves and hesitations aside to nod one more time. "Really."

*   *   *

The heavy, anxious feeling in my stomach didn't go away for days. Tyler invited me out on a couple of dates, which I thought seemed a little redundant since we already knew each other. The first was to go out stargazing and the second to watch the sunset, which I thought seemed a little clichéd. Thankfully, it rained both times and I was able to get out of them. Stargazing was something I also took very seriously, and that wasn't an experience I necessarily wanted to share with him. For me, it was about connection and questions and observation, not an excuse to start making out or pretend to know which constellation was which in order to seem impressive—that would be an insult to me. If I wanted to go stargazing it would be because I genuinely *wanted* to gaze at stars.

I was particularly tired today, having cleaned more than my usual number of rooms since other RAs were beginning to leave for home or transfer to other parts of the hotel—no surprise there. I cleaned what I needed to clean, helped where I needed to help, then grabbed some odd combination of food at the EDR, where I currently was. After eating, I planned to take a nice hot shower, crawl into my bed, and watch *You've Got Mail* on DVD with Meg Ryan and Tom Hanks. That would be my paradise.

Mid-bite, Tyler plopped his tray down next to mine at our group's usual table. "Hey, what are you doing tonight?"

"Watching a movie in bed and that's about it."

"Great," he said, "I'll come over to your room after changing."

I looked at him. "You know that's a chick flick, right?" hoping to steer him away.

He shrugged. "That's fine."

Something about him being okay with that seemed a little suspicious, but I let it go. Maybe he really didn't mind chick flicks. If my dad liked watching *Love, Actually* at Christmastime, then maybe Tyler liked *You've Got Mail*. I don't know.

I let out a sigh. "Okay, just come by whenever."

*   *   *

The two of us sat on my bed with our backs against the wall and feet dangling off the side. Since Sarah was gone, we had the room to ourselves, which was probably why Tyler wanted to come over in the first place. Throughout the entirety of the film, all I could think about was how bored he must have been.

A little more than halfway through the movie, he asked me, "Are you comfortable?"

I nodded. "Yeah, I'm good."

Meg Ryan had begun to befriend Tom Hanks. She'd already gone through all the drama of resenting him for attempting to ruin her small bookshop by putting a massive, corporatized Fox Books just down the street from her. They were in the park together now, dissecting all the emails she'd received over the course of the movie from her internet boyfriend who— spoiler alert—happened to be Tom Hanks.

"Are you comfortable?" Tyler asked again, ten minutes later.

"Yes," I answered, not entirely sure why he was so concerned with my comfort.

"Do you want to be more comfortable?"

I looked over at him, confused. "What do you mean?"

"I mean..." he trailed off, gesturing to his arm he had opened, inviting me to rest against him.

"Oh," I said, scooting over to him. "Okay."

Something about this felt awkward and unfamiliar. I didn't really know what to do with the arm that was pressed into him, so I just sort of draped it over my waist. He rested his arm over my shoulder, his hand hanging down just over my left shoulder. We sat like that until the credits started rolling. By then, I had slipped significantly farther down the bed to the point where my chin practically rested on my collarbone.

This can't be how this is supposed to feel, I thought to myself. For some reason, though, I felt nervous about readjusting myself. Taking a big breath in, I forced myself to do it anyway, reorienting myself on the mattress, my back farther up against the wall now.

Neither of us said anything. We just watched the music play and the credits roll. I saw him turn to me out of the corner of my eye. Ignoring this, I suddenly began rattling off facts about the movie.

"Hey, did you know that all the emails were uploaded to a real Warner Brothers website? So, you could actually read through them all if you wanted to," I said.

"That's cool," he said, unimpressed, and continuing to gaze at me.

"And Meg Ryan, the main character, actually worked in that bookshop to get prepared for her role. I mean I wouldn't mind doing that if I were her, being surrounded by all those books."

Tyler, clueing into what I was doing, asked, "Is this awkward for you? Kinda seems like you're stalling."

And the sky is blue and the earth is round.

"I just don't really know what I'm doing," I admitted, attempting to laugh it off.

"Have you ever had a boyfriend?" he asked.

I could feel my cheeks turning bright red. I shook my head. "No."

His eyes widened into saucers. "*Really?* Ever?"

"Ever."

"So..." he said, thinking aloud, "does that mean you've never been kissed before?"

I suddenly began to feel very hot with embarrassment. I had mixed emotions about this conversation; I wanted my inexperience to be noticed, but I didn't want it to reflect poorly on me. I was a prude and I knew it, but I didn't want to be seen as "less than" because of it.

"No," I said, avoiding his eyes.

"Why not?"

I shrugged. "I don't know, just never happened, I guess."

He shifted closer to me, crushing my arm a bit more. "Do you want to have your first with me?"

My heart was pounding like a hydraulic press if it were jacked up to a hundred beats a minute. I thought about it, figuring that if I did, I could just get the whole thing out of the way and not have to worry about it ever again with anyone else.

"Okay," I said, my voice coming out more like a whisper than a regular speaking tone.

We turned to face each other, him more than me. I could feel his breath warming the air between us. I wondered what I might look like to him—short brown lashes, pale skin, blackheads sprinkled across my nose, scared eyes.

I leaned in first, more as an attempt to get it over with, as I closed my eyes and tilted my head. I found his mouth and did what came naturally. The scruff of his skin scratched my chin.

What I didn't feel, though, was a spark, something I thought was supposed to happen with your first kiss. This one was blank, an unaddressed envelope meant for no one. I guess I just thought it would be, like, *more* somehow.

We kissed for another breath or two before pulling away. If anything, I felt more mature, but mostly relieved.

Tyler looked at me with hopeful, blue eyes, his long, ginger lashes blinking, awaiting my response. "So? What did you think?"

"It felt…different. But it was good," I fibbed.

"Good," he smiled before leaning back.

Later that night, I texted Sarah and told her what had happened. She said she was happy for me. I wondered why I didn't feel the same.

CHAPTER 16

·· • ✦ • ✦ • ··

To my surprise, I didn't have a hangover. If anything, I woke up with a slight buzz from the night before, which I didn't even realize was possible until someone made a comment on how loopy I was still acting.

I spent three hours at the pub with Candice and Tyler last night for my birthday. I asked Candice to come, mostly because I didn't trust Tyler enough to leave him in charge of me if-slash-when I became incapacitated. He did give me one piece of advice, though: "The rule for turning twenty-one is that you never buy your own drinks."

When word got out, people I didn't even know were buying me so many shots I couldn't remember who gave me which ones. My head was swimming by eleven o'clock as I listened to three random guys at the bar sing "Happy Birthday" in a very slurred, but enthusiastic way. By eleven-thirty, Candice was holding my hair as I puked into the toilet in one of the bathroom stalls. By a quarter to midnight, I had my head buried in a public trash can and was told by the bouncer there that I needed to go home.

Back in my room, I drunk cried about nothing to Candice and Tyler. That part I remember because of how pathetic I felt. Tyler at least talked about nothing with his head inside of his pillowcase when he got home after his twenty-first at the pub.

His birthday was just two days before and almost everyone was there for it, including Dorian and Gretchen, before they left for home. He was toast by eleven and kept pointing at me, saying things like, "Isn't she cute?" and "I wish Lauren would take my pants off."

For the past week and a half, we'd been spending a lot of time together. Nothing had happened, but he would often convince me to do things I wasn't comfortable with and make odd requests. When I would say no, he'd attempt to seduce me into giving in, but I'd usually deflect until he moved on to something else.

Every hour we spent together pushed me further away from him. I found him less and less appealing and I found our time together to be more strenuous the longer it went on. I wanted my room back, my space back, my time back, but never knew how to ask for that. Each kiss became scratchier, each interaction became more uncomfortable, and it all me very uncomfortable. But I continued with it because I assumed it all to be normal. I trusted the experience of being with him as best I could, despite how much it weighed on me.

Thankfully, I'd be leaving tomorrow. Most of my stuff was packed and piled into my car, including my bedsheets. The only thing remaining was my duffel bag, which sat on the floor by the door.

The smooth nylon interior of my sleeping bag kept me warm on my stripped mattress as I thought about everything. It was midnight and I couldn't get my brain to shut off, so I lay on my side staring out the window on the far side of the room, out at the world I'd be leaving behind. I thought about Tyler, my birthday, my friends, my job, and my transition back into real life. Part of me was excited, though. I had something special and important to bring back with me: an *experience*, and one that was probably unlike anything anyone else I'd known had ever done. I was the second of two in my entire family to have done something like this. All I could do was put it in my pocket and bring as much of it as I could back home.

SEASON II

CHAPTER 17

‒‒‒‒‒‒‒‒‒‒ ···✦✦✦··· ‒‒‒‒‒‒‒‒‒‒

I thought I was supposed to enjoy being home. Turns out I was wrong. It was fun for a brief period when I was running high on life with the pocketed memory of the beautiful season of my life, but I was often met with indifference.

For three months, I received texts, phone calls, and tagged posts on social media from friends boasting about how proud of me they were and how they couldn't wait for me to come back home. Then when I did, no one reached out; I was the one to initiate lunches, coffee dates, meet-ups. It felt like no one showed genuine curiosity toward my summer and everything I learned, how I grew, and what I saw. They acted exactly the same, as if it didn't make a difference to them one way or another.

That's one thing they don't tell you—how shitty it feels to come home to everything being exactly the same when, all the while, you thought people would have grown as much as you had. It's like Plato's "Allegory of the Cave" when that one guy escapes the cave that is representative of a life he *perceives* and discovers a whole new world outside it, but by escaping and coming back to talk about all that he's seen, he's labeled the insane one.

I made plans to catch up with a friend around the time school started, just a couple weeks after getting back. I'd known her since high school, and she would be transferring to my university for our junior year. We decided to meet up at a whimsical little diner downtown for lunch in our college town, forty-five minutes away from home.

"*Hiiii!*" she squealed when she finally saw me, throwing her hands around my neck in an embrace. She always had what you might call a loud personality—bouncy brown hair, trendy outfits, and always traveled with a pack of friends, except for today. Today, it was just us.

"Heyyy," I chimed, hugging her back, "it's so good to see you!"

"You too, wild thang! You better tell me everything. I've been *dying* to know how it all went!" she said as we both walked inside and found our seats in a little booth.

Nothing about this restaurant was ordinary—each table had its own unique tablecloth, each mug was a different size and shape, and each chair was a new style and color. I learned that when it first opened a year ago, most items were donations from the Salvation Army next door, which is why the diner was so eclectic. Our tablecloth was patterned blue and yellow, with a thick turquoise border around the square cloth and quaint little flowers printed around the middle.

"It was amazing," I started, taking my seat, "I don't really even know where to begin. You saw most of the stuff that I posted on Facebook, right?"

"Yes!"

"Well, the internet there sucked, first of all, there was like no Wi-Fi, so that was really hard to do. But it was mostly just a lot of working and hiking. The work got pretty gross at times and the hikes could be brutal, but there was this—I don't know—almost *majestic* quality about everything," I explained, trying to find the right words to describe what I meant. I continued along with all the things I saw, experienced, and learned, rambling on for a good few minutes.

"That sounds amazing," she smiled, flicking her long, wavy brown hair over her shoulder. "Literally *perfect*. Actually, I got Princess a new cat toy and mostly hung out with Taz. By the way, he and I are actually gonna try living together this year. You remember him, right?"

I was both caught off guard by her sudden switch of topics and surprised by her decision to move in with her boyfriend. "Oh. Yeah, I think I met him once. I thought you were dating Johnny?"

She contorted her face into something indicating disgust. "Ick. No, we broke up at the beginning of the summer. Didn't ever wanna do anything except get stoned. I mean, I do too sometimes, y'know? But there's a limit and he just kept getting lazier and lazier. But anyway, yeah, Taz and I are gonna be living about a mile from campus."

I faked a smile but did my best to make it feel genuine. "That's great. If you're happy, I'm happy."

Our waitress then came up requesting our drink orders, briefly apologizing for the wait as it was a busy lunch hour.

Something about sitting here with this friend I've known for years, listening to her talking about her boyfriend, her cat, and her new apartment, unsettled me. I was seeing a side of her that ultimately showed disinterest in a wild experience people my age rarely ever get to have. But why? She asked about me, about Yellowstone, and I told her. Yet, throughout the duration of our lunch date, I asked more follow-up questions about her life than she did about mine.

That's when I realized that when people say they can't wait to see you or want to have you back, they mean they can't wait to have you back in the *vicinity*. They want to be comforted by your presence, knowing you're just a phone call or text away. If she wanted to see me and not just confirm that I made it home safely, *she* would have reached out first instead of me. *She* would have asked questions out of genuine curiosity. Instead, I was sitting across from someone I considered a close friend, listening to her tell me about her new cat toy when I was the one sitting there with a two-million-acre national park in my hands, wanting to show it all to her.

Lunch lasted barely an hour. I think we ran out of things to talk about. Walking over to my car afterward, I noticed how much smaller the town looked. It wasn't that large to begin with, but I began to reflect on all that was available for me there: the line of bars on Pine Street, the local Walmart, and Applebee's. The town didn't have much, and most of my friends there were under twenty-one, which meant even if I wanted to go out and have a night of fun, it'd be tricky. My social life had been reduced from hiking mountains and hammocking between centuries-old pines to study groups and half-priced appetizers on Wednesday nights.

I knew not many people would understand this. The high from Yellowstone only lasted a couple of weeks before wearing off at the start of school when it turned to depletion and, later, to depression. The only person I really felt I could talk to was Candice, with whom I read poetry and drank coffee by the Yellowstone Lake, but she was way over in Texas while I lived in Missouri. Ever since our little outings, I felt like I could tell her anything and she would just *get* it. I think she felt the same way too because we'd occasionally Skype to talk about where we were in our lives and how unhappy we were with it, wishing we were back in the sweet embrace of the western pines.

"You know, Lauren, it's normal to feel that way," Dad said one night as we sat on the porch together, exactly where I was before my whole adventure started. I'd opened up to him about the disconnect I'd been feeling after telling him all about my adventures—hiking, working, sightseeing, wildlife-watching…

"When I came back, a little over thirty years ago, I knew things would never be the same again. Even then I knew," he said.

It was like a riddle very few of us could understand. Was it possible for the place you love to, in fact, become your same cause of death?

I felt I was constantly pulled in two different directions. Being home meant I'd need to reduce myself to everything I was before in order to fit back in; it was possible, though difficult, but I didn't want to do it. The person I became back in the mountains—brave, honest, and for once, *cracked open*— was the person I always wanted to be, though embodying that person meant sacrificing the image others had of me as sweet, dutiful, respectable.

I felt torn between who I was and who I was *supposed* to be.

It wasn't until one cold November day that Dorian emailed me on Facebook, asking if I'd thought about returning to Yellowstone. Truthfully, I hadn't. If I was to return to the parks, I'd want to do someplace different, like Glacier National Park in Montana. Being the pre-law student he was, he convinced me to give it another shot and that we could work together to recruit some people. Candice, as it would later seem, was the only other person interested enough to consider it.

Only the three of us returned.

CHAPTER 18

···✦✦✦···

You know how dogs whine and paw at the door when they see something outside they want really badly, like a squirrel or a bird? Then when you let them out, they take off at lightning speed, dashing past you and out into the open world? That's what leaving home felt like.

But instead of my ears flapping in the wind, it was my hair. All the windows were open as "Baba O'Riley" by The Who was playing on the radio just as the soft outline of the Wyoming mountains began to take shape along the horizon. They were *my* mountains.

The sun was shining on this day in mid-May and I was headed toward Gardiner from Livingston, Montana, where I stayed in another ridiculously expensive Super 8 last night. Candice and I had made an agreement to room together in Pelican a few months ago. She'd be waiting for me since she got in right when the season opened a month ago, and Dorian would be coming in a few days after me. He'd just gotten back from studying in England for the past year. Nothing that guy did surprised me anymore. He could tell me he had tea with the queen herself and I'd believe him.

I was feeling better than I had in a long time. I felt whole again. All the stress and worry I felt a year ago driving down this same stretch on Highway 90 had completely dissolved. I knew exactly what I was getting into, and this time with a pay raise. I was returning as an inspector.

On either side of me were rolling hills and grassy plains, muted shades of gold and mint with scattered clusters of lush tumbleweeds. For miles, you could see nothing but the grasses and the faint blue outline of the Wyoming mountains along the never-ending horizon. My car was filled with the vague scent of pine, most likely carried over by the wind from the distant forests.

I was almost home.

An hour later, in the gravel parking lot outside of Yellowstone's Human Resources building in Gardiner, just north of the park, I received a text from Candice that would completely sour my mood.

The HR people here put me with a new roommate just so you know.

It wasn't that long ago when I was leaving Livingston that I told her I was on my way and couldn't wait to room with her. To say this was a surprise would be an understatement. Sitting in my car, my eyebrows scrunched up at the screen as I began typing back my response on the virtual keyboard.

What? Didn't they know we'd be rooming together? I asked, remembering how I included her name on my application this past winter in the section for roommate requests.

A few seconds later, she responded. *Idk man, you'll have to check with them when you get here. She's pretty cool tho, you'd like her.*

As if *that* would remedy the weight of this major inconvenience.

What do you want me to do with all the stuff I brought?

Before leaving, I asked if there was anything she wanted or needed, since I knew the nearest grocery store was two hours east. She requested an extra pillow, hair ties, snacks, even a coffee pot, and I'd brought it all along just for her. It was sitting in a bag in the backseat of my car.

You can still bring it all over or I can pick it up, it doesn't matter, she said. *I'm in 218.*

I didn't respond. I didn't know what else to say. A large part of me wished I could've been more candid with her about how much this last-minute change bothered me, especially when I was only an hour and a half away from Lake out of a seventeen-hour drive. What stopped me from pressing her even harder about this was the fact that, besides Dorian, she was the only other person I knew, and I held our friendship very close to my heart. She was, after all, the first writer, poet, and daydreamer I'd ever met, and I couldn't afford to wreck that. If I did, I'd be lonely all over again. It'd be devastating.

On the drive down, I made a wish: to meet more good people, to meet new friends who would stay in touch for longer than just a few months. Not long after the end of last season, everyone just sort of scattered to the winds. Dorian, Candice, and Tyler were the only people I really stayed connected with. Now I'm here, just barely having arrived in Yellowstone, and the first friend's already fallen through. I was beginning to fear I would need to start all over again, to be miserable for the first two weeks before my little world would come together again.

Not knowing entirely what to do with myself now, confidence depleted, I sat. I sat in resentment, aggravation, and disappointment. I stayed like that until, finally, I took a deep breath in, stepped out of my car, and pushed myself walk up to the screen door, tossing it open and following the arrows to a check-in desk via arrows stickered to the thin, basil-colored carpet.

Stepping into what was a very long line, I noticed how there was an unusually high number of men present. The only females I could find were either HR employees or sprinkled within the groups of men. Checking twice to make sure I was in the right place, I could only assume that, well, I was. Two more guys stepped in behind me.

It was forty-five minutes before I could even see the check-in desk. I decided now might be a good idea to check my bag to make sure I had everything I needed. My fingers located my wallet, positioning it toward the light above just enough so that I could make out my driver's license displayed in the clear pocket on the side. Then, searching at the bottom of the heap, in every pocket, and even the outside one for my second form of identification, I quickly realized something majorly important: I'd left my social security card at home.

My stomach instantly dropped and my breath caught in my throat. My ears grew hot with panic.

I continued shuffling around again anyway, occasionally pausing to think if there was anything else I had back in the car that would work, but I knew my social security card was the only thing that was going to get me in. That or a passport, which, obviously, I didn't have either. I immediately began envisioning the secretary's face as she turned me away, kicking me out of the park and slapping me with a hefty fine for attempted fraud or something.

I was what they'd call SOL—Shit Outta Luck.

Not entirely sure what else to do, I snatched my phone out from my back pocket to text my mom. My fingers, nervous and alert, tapped at the screen as I glanced up at the desk again to gauge how much time I had. All in caps, I wrote, *I FORGOT MY SOCIAL SECURITY CARD.*

A second later, I felt my phone vibrate. *Ok, I'll ship it over tomorrow. In the meantime, tell her ur returning. U should be in the system,* she wrote, more casually than I expected.

Not feeling any better, I looked up at the two guys in front of me, staring at the backs of their shirts, attempting to muster up the courage to speak to them. Finally, I heard myself ask, "Are you guys returners?"

Glancing over their shoulders at me, they nodded. "Yeah?" one of them said with a quizzical look.

"Okay, so then they should already have you in the system, right? Like if you forgot anything, they should have all your stuff on file?" I asked, gesturing to the woman at the desk up front.

They looked at each other, not really sure how to respond. I could've guessed based on their expressions: *Wow, get a load of this chick. What a newbie.*

"I mean, I don't know. That's kind of tricky. You could try it and see what happens," the same guy said, shrugging. "Hope things work out for ya, though."

"Thanks."

So that was helpful.

At a loss, I decided to distract myself by fidgeting profusely and counting the steps I thought it would take to reach the desk. My palms were growing hot and damp. Finally, fifteen minutes later, when it was my turn to step up, the lady looked at me with an expectant look, not saying anything.

"Hi," I initiated, feeling as relaxed as a Wall Street stock trader. "So, I'm a returner from last year, but left my social security card at home. Is there any way my mom might be able to ship it over to you guys overnight or something?"

Her eyebrows scrunched together in concern. "Ooh, that might be a little tricky. What's the name?"

For a second, I thought she meant my mom's.

"Lauren Erickson," I said, my voice ending more like a question rather than a statement as I'd intended.

Her fingernails clicked against the chunky black keyboard while her elderly eyes swam around the screen behind her thick bifocals.

"Yep, there you are," she said after a minute. "You got an ID?"

As quickly as I could manage, I fished my license out from my purse and handed it over to her, watching her look back and forth from the plastic card to the computer screen before she handed it back.

"You're in the system, but I'd like to get Rob over here to take a quick look at this." Picking up the radio she had on her desk, she dropped to a monotone to call for Rob before rattling off some code numbers.

I turned my head to the side and used my peripheral vision to get a peek at the long line of people accumulating behind me. Guilt festered in my chest.

Rob walked in from around the corner. The lady explained the situation to him as he looked at the same screen, putting his hands loosely on his hips, occasionally nodding.

"Mm. Yeah, that *is* tricky," he repeated.

Today wanted me to suffer.

"What's your date of birth?" Rob asked, peering at me over the frame of his thick glasses.

"August 5, 1996."

"And you said you left your social security card back home?"

"Yes."

He nodded once. "Okay. So, since nothing has really changed and we have all your information in the system, we're gonna let you slide," he said. "But if you decide to come back for another season, you're gonna need to bring that information, okay? It's really important that we have it."

"Yes, sir. I totally understand," I said.

Rob walked back to whatever corner of the room he came from, and the check-in lady instructed me to sit on the waiting bench in the middle of the room with the others to wait for my Terrego-issued employee ID.

Simultaneously relieved and irritated with myself, I inhaled the deepest breath I could and let it all out until my stomach couldn't flex anymore. Five minutes later, I was called over to another spot in the large room, against a white wall, to get my picture taken for my ID. They handed me a few other clerical documents and sent me out the door to another building next door for my uniform fitting.

If I didn't remember its location from last year, it would've taken me forever to find it. It was located in what almost looked like a loading station for semi-trucks or something. It was a large gravel lot with miscellaneous trailers scattered around, and the one I needed was, of course, the farthest away.

The fitting process was much longer than it really needed to be, between the awkward male trouser proportions on a female body and the missing buttons that kept my oversized work blouse indecent.

An hour and a half later, I was back on the road again, driving onward through Mammoth and down the east end to Lake. I knew this route like the back of my hand. Doing my best to push the negativity of the day's events aside, between the check-in scare and Candice's text, I popped in a CD I'd burned before leaving and did my best to sing along.

CHAPTER 19

⋯⋅✦✦✦⋅⋯

"Hey, Lauren!"

It was Kyle from HR with his cool, sandy voice and monotonous tone, except this time, he said my name with more animation than I'd ever seen. "Back for another season?" he asked, tilting back into his chair as it let out a small squeak.

I nodded, taking a seat in one of the two chairs in front of his desk. The second desk next to Kyle's was empty. "Yeah, Yellowstone part two. I'm also supposed to be rooming with Candice."

"You are?" Kyle shuffled some papers around on his desk, pausing to look at a couple of different ones. "Hm...doesn't look like it. I have that she's rooming with someone named Emmy."

This confirmed everything: Candice had swapped me out for another roommate.

Disappointment spilled into my bloodstream and chest all over again. I was sure I'd written her name down on my application as a suggested roommate, and I *know* we made plans by text to do that. It was also confusing since we'd spent hours talking over Skype about how out of place we felt since being back home, how it was more difficult to find our rhythm again, and how we wished we could go back to the mountains. And now that we were here, plans were suddenly shifted, changed, altered, and Candice didn't seem to want to do anything to remedy that, which indirectly told me that she didn't mind not rooming with me.

"Want me to put you back in Pelican again?" Kyle asked. My expression must have looked a little worried because he quickly added, "Don't worry. I won't drop another pin."

I nodded. "Yeah, sure."

He scratched his bald head, eyes still heavy and lazy as he flipped through the pile of paperwork on his desk. "Well, since we don't have anyone else here to claim as your roommate, looks like you're just gonna have to wait until I can find you one. By the way, you got any papers for me?"

"Yes," I said, hiding the disappointment from my voice, and handed him a wrinkled collection of various colored documents.

Once I was able to leave, I walked back up the long gravel path, across the main road, and toward the dorms on the other side. I'd already parked my car by Pelican because that's where all the dorms were anyway and they really weren't all that strict about checking for the employee sticker that was supposed to go on your car. I still needed to renew mine for this year.

Everything looked pretty much the same. Dark chocolate wood, thick walls of trees around every building, even the picnic bench out front for the smokers was in its usual spot. One by one, I began bringing in boxes, tubs, and armfuls of camp supplies, clothes, bedding, toiletries, and snacks.

About an hour into unpacking and setting up my end of the room, snagging the bed by the window this time, I heard the door squeak open on the other side of the bathroom and watched two fresh faces walk in. It almost looked like they came together based on how they were talking with each other, immersed in conversation and smiles. One of the girls reminded me an awful lot of Rachel McAdams—a tall, heart-shaped face, light brown hair, and wisdom in her smile. The other was much quieter and equally as gorgeous with thick, wavy locks that curled in all the right places and a long, dark set of lashes I could see from the other side of the room. She threw a copy of *1984* by George Orwell onto one of the beds while lugging in her suitcases.

The first one who looked like Rachel McAdams must have heard me messing with a zipper on my duffel bag because she poked her head through the bathroom doorway and noticed me.

"Oh, hey," she waved as she let all her stuff drop to the floor. "I'm Sophia."

"Oh, hi," I answered, like I'd just noticed they'd walked in. "I'm Lauren, nice to meet you."

The George Orwell girl popped her head around from their open door. "I'm Skylar," she waved with a light voice. "Nice to meet you!" She seemed very sweet and bubbly.

"Hi, Skylar," I waved back. "Where are you guys from?"

"Georgia."

"Tennessee."

"Oh, you don't know each other?"

They paused to look at each other. "No," Sophia replied with a soft laugh. "We just got back from HR and this guy there just sorta randomly put us together."

I smiled to myself, knowing exactly what she was talking about. "Did he ask if you were quiet?"

She looked at me in surprise. "Yeah, actually."

"Then did he drop a pin?"

"*Yeah.*"

"Welcome to Lake," I chuckled.

She laughed, probably not entirely sure of what I meant by that, and walked over to her new side of the room to grab a water bottle. "So, where's your roommate? Or are you getting one later?"

"Well..." I started, thinking of the right words to say, "I was supposed to room with someone I worked with last season, but it fell through at the last minute. I'll probably end up getting someone random."

"Oh, that's too bad. So, this isn't your first time then?"

I shook my head. "No, it's my second."

Sophia must've felt a little self-conscious after hearing me say that because she tried to backpedal out of it. "Oh, gotcha. Yeah, this is our first, so we're pretty new. We'll figure it out, though, it'll be fine," she chuckled, waving her hand like it wasn't a big deal.

"It's really not that bad. It might be a little rough for the first couple of weeks, but it gets better. I can show you guys around later or something if you want, too," I said, hoping to ease their nerves.

They both smiled wide. "That would be great!" Sophia said.

*   *   *

Orientation was the next day. I signed up to be an inspector with Dorian this season, hoping we'd be able to spend another summer out in the cabins. Fully prepared to learn the do's and don'ts of housekeeping again, I made my way up to the same second-floor conference room of the hotel when Claire approached me to, essentially, persuade me to skip inspector training with a mentor and start independently tomorrow since they were so understaffed. According to her, they had maybe four inspectors and seven room attendants for all of Lake—the hotel, the smaller Sandpiper motel, and cabins.

"Danica and I will train you along the way," she said, almost like a plea. As usual, she was carrying her clipboard and radio with her hair up in one of those casual fan buns on top of her head. Her icy eyes were still highlighted by that same thick, black liner.

"I guess I'm just not sure what I'm supposed to be doing yet," I admitted, feeling unsure and unprepared.

She shrugged. "All you're doing is double-checking the rooms and making sure they're clean. You'll occasionally help the RAs with stripping beds and stuff. We know you won't be perfect; we've got time to teach you, but we need all hands on deck right now."

I figured I'd be doing those things, but my question was more around *how*. Was there any particular way or order in which I needed to check the rooms? How did I lead a team of room attendants? What about those mid-afternoon meetings I sometimes saw them have? What about all those numbers they typed into the computer in the back of the cabin office?

I reached for the ring on my middle finger and started twisting it. It was obvious she needed help and an immediate answer, like she couldn't wait another minute before brushing me off and asking for help from someone else.

"Okay," I decided at last, acting more willing than I actually felt. "Sure, I can help."

Claire's shoulders visibly relaxed. "Great, great." She nodded with an exhale. "Well, you can just meet me in the office tomorrow morning then and we'll go over it."

"Usual time as last season? Eight o'clock?"

"Seven forty-five," she said before walking off.

When I showed up the next morning, I must have missed something because the little closet of an office was filled with all the other inspectors shuffling around, grabbing radios, lists, highlighters, and pens, like a New York City cafe during morning rush hour. I tiptoed from the main area into the manager's office, careful not to step on the people squatting on the ground highlighting small piles of stapled papers since there were hardly any chairs for them to sit in.

Claire was inside sitting at her desk, which was littered with more papers than I'd ever seen. An extra pen was shoved into her bun. I watched her with caution before greeting her in a voice higher than I anticipated.

"Hi."

She jumped at that and immediately looked up. "Oh, hey, Lauren," she said, flipping through some of the papers before locating a few stapled sheets with three different names scrawled on them, one of them being mine. "So this is your master list and these two RAs are on your team today. Candice can show you what to do with these. She should be right outside."

Something seemed off. I was missing something. I got we were understaffed, but what was the rush for? I was told to be here at a quarter to eight and I was, but I somehow felt like I showed up much later than I needed to. In fact, it felt like I was very, very late.

With the minimal instructions I received from Claire, I took the three sets of stapled papers and flipped through them, realizing they were the list of room assignments I used to work from last season.

Candice, whom I spotted on the floor by her messy blonde bun, was sitting with a few other inspectors. She was preoccupied with flipping her papers and scraping three different colored highlighters across her papers. "Hey, Lo. You get your lists?" That was the nickname she had given me toward the end of last season.

"Yeah," I nodded.

"Okay, so this one right here is the master list where you can see all the rooms your RAs will be servicing. These two other papers are for your team and their names are in the top right corner. Any row that says 'Due-Out' is highlighted pink, 'Occupied' is yellow, and 'No Service' is green. We're doing this new thing called 'Softer Footprint' where we don't service those rooms unless it's requested. It's basically like a DND," she explained, referring to the "Do Not Disturb" signs guests sometimes hung from their doorknobs.

As she spoke, I followed along in my head with mental bullet points, *Pink bad, yellow good, green best.* "Okay," I said, "I can do that."

She continued. "Then you highlight those respective colors from your RA's room lists on the master list on your clipboard. See, look at mine: This room, 220, is pink because it's a due-out that needs to be fully serviced, and I've highlighted that same room number in pink on my master sheet so I have a record of it. Also, if I were you, I'd "X" out the rooms that you finish instead of scribbling them out so you can see which ones they are in case management asks about it."

Beginning to feel a little overwhelmed, I stayed with her and did my best to remember everything she said. *Highlight everything and always "X",* I silently translated to myself.

We sat together on the floor of the office, highlighting as fast as we could, trying to keep up with the pace of everyone else, me more than her. Candice's lists were nearly complete, so she finished about thirty seconds before me, getting up to grab herself a radio and tossing another over to me while I remained on the floor, attempting to balance three markers in one hand as I rushed to remember which rows to highlight.

"Usually around this time we'll head up to the conference room to pass the sheets out to our team and do all the regular meeting stuff, so it's best to get here a little earlier."

I felt beyond flustered, and it wasn't even eight in the morning yet. "Hey, wait, how do I know where I'm working today?" I asked.

"Top of the room assignments," she said, heading toward the door.

Looking down at the top of my papers, I saw in black ink, "Lake Hotel: East Wing" stamped out in Arial font. That was my last choice and the place I had the least experience cleaning. Management would have an even closer eye on me, and because of that, I wouldn't be able to listen to music. Further, some of the rooms were twice as big as the cabins, which meant it would take nearly twice as long to clean.

A heavy weight of dread began to form in the pit of my stomach.

Nearly the last one left in the office, I clipped the radio Candice tossed me onto my front pants pocket, grabbed my clipboard, and highlighted my way out the door like a high schooler rushing to complete forgotten homework on the way to class during passing period.

*   *   *

Our day ended the latest that it ever had: eight o'clock at night. More than a twelve-hour day. My feet ached so badly, I could feel them scream at me with every step I took. The soles of my feet were more tender than they had ever been. I could step on the world's fluffiest cloud and still wince in pain.

I pulled my phone out of my front pocket to check my health stats and it reported I'd walked nearly nine miles today. Nearly *nine* miles of grabbing and hauling supplies for my two housekeepers' carts so they wouldn't need to waste time doing that, running up and down the stairs for extra coffee mugs and spoons because only guests could use the elevators, racing in and out of fifteen rooms, inspecting and calling them in from the telephones on the nightstand.

I didn't know what I was doing for most of the day. Danica, who was still assistant manager, hardly checked on me. She only gave me a couple of pointers to tide me over for the day. "Check to make sure everything's in its place and have them redo it if you don't think it's good enough," she'd said at one point before twirling around in her sundress to go check on the other inspectors. That much I understood, yes, but it was the operational details I still lacked.

Mary, however, appeared to be gone and an RA from last season, had taken her place as the second assistant manager.

The goal I'd set for myself today was to have at least five rooms done by lunch. It would've been more, but there was only so much a team of two RAs could accomplish. On a good day, someone could do three rooms if they weren't too dirty, and with a trainer, they could complete four or more.

Truthfully, my job was more than I could handle. I felt like I needed to be everywhere all at once, but I couldn't be. The guests needed me, the RAs needed me, and management needed me, but what about me? I needed someone just as much as they did and I didn't have anyone to turn to for training—not even Candice, who was out in the cabins today.

Why was it that everything needed to be so high stakes out here? I mean, not just the job, but also the partying, the hiking, the rules and regulations—if you messed up once, you messed up completely. I knew people who had gotten kicked out less than twenty-four hours after being caught drinking underage, and I knew people who knew people who had gotten killed by getting too close to a cliff or a bison or a geyser. It was my first day on the job and felt like I was expected to know what I was doing even though I really, *really* didn't. Management could appear at any moment, around any corner, and want a status update or give me another task to complete, and *I* felt responsible for giving it to them at the very moment they needed it.

But I also knew how hypocritical the park could be. I knew of people who did unethical things to get promotions. I knew people in management who did hard drugs, including cocaine, and got away with it. I knew women my age who felt they were being harassed by their creepy, old bosses in other parts of the hotel. But they never got caught. It was never high stakes for anyone in management. Only for people like me.

CHAPTER 20

····◆◆◆··

On my third day of work, right when I was developing a vague sense of my inspector duties, HR called Claire in the housekeeping office who radioed me to report to them. It was ten in the morning, right when many of the guests began leaving their rooms for the day and housekeeping could really get to work.

"Don't worry," Claire told me. I was talking with her on the telephone in one of the hotel rooms I'd just inspected. "I'll radio Sanchez and have him cover for you."

This made me feel even worse because that meant he'd be carrying both my duties *and* his this morning—he'd have double the work to do while I was gone. Sanchez was a nice guy and I knew him from last year too, so I felt a little at fault for putting the extra weight on him, even though I had minimal control over what would be today's fiasco.

"What about my RAs?" I asked.

"He'll tell them what to do," she promised.

I hung up the phone then made my way down the stairs to the first floor, past the deli shop, and out the back door toward that same old white trailer, kicking up dust and getting gravel in my shoes on the walk there.

Inside, I expected to see dry-humored Kyle with his protruding Adam's apple inside, but instead I was greeted by a wispy, vaguely pedophilic mustache and a purple puffer vest. It was a youngish guy—probably in his early or mid-thirties—named Brandon, according to his name tag. He looked new, but he very well could've transferred from another area of the park to Lake.

He looked up with a half-smile that made me a little uncomfortable. "Hey, Lauren. How are things?"

"Fine, I guess," I replied, feeling a little tense.

"Good, good to hear," he said, scooching his chair toward his desk before easing back into it. "So listen, I was getting your file all squared away when I noticed there wasn't a copy of your social security card or passport on file."

I gave him a funny look, suddenly confused. "Yeah, there was a bit of a complication checking in back in Gardiner, but they were gonna let it slide since I was already in the system. They said they were going to call you about it."

Brandon's eyebrows scrunched together as he glanced at the papers on his desk. "Hm," he said with fake speculation. "Well, I haven't gotten any calls from them, and we still don't have any type of copy on file, so…"

I didn't know what else to tell him, so I continued to tell the truth. "I don't know, they just told me they'd let it slide this time. I offered to have my mom FedEx it over, but there didn't seem to be any need for that."

"Right, but here's the thing," he said, sitting up from his chair to lean toward me with his hands clasped together on top of his desk, "it's super important that we have this. If we don't have it within the next three days to send up to Gardiner for clearance, then our only choice will be to terminate you."

I sat in silence, my cheeks getting red with fear and a tiny inkling of aggravation. It wasn't until this moment that I'd forgotten about how broken the communication here was. Why couldn't they just phone them? Email them to double-check? Brandon continued to look at me, waiting. When I didn't say anything, he spoke again.

"If you have someone who could have it shipped to us by Monday then that would reserve your employment status. UPS tends to take a while with shipments, so I would suggest FedEx-ing it overnight. It'll take a couple of extra days to make its way down here, since we're a national park and are a little more remote."

My blood turned bitter as I forced what politeness I had reserved to slide off my tongue. "Sure. Like I said, I offered to do that up in Gardiner, but they said they were gonna let it slide. I could have my mom do it, though."

"Great," he smiled, leaning back in his chair, satisfied with my answer. "Does she have an email address I could reach her at?"

As I gave him her information, I watched his languid fingers click across the keyboard. It was all I could do not to imagine his puffer vest as inflated, purple peacock wings while he did so.

"I'm going to tell her to scan a copy of it to send to me while we're waiting for it just as a temporary fix," he explained, not taking his eyes off the screen.

"Why wouldn't that work?"

"Because we need the real deal for authenticity purposes."

Then what's the point? I wondered. "I'll give my mom a call," I said, pulling out my phone.

"Oh, and another thing," he added, his eyes catching mine before letting me go, "since this is more of a bigger issue we're dealing with, we're gonna ask you to take a temporary leave of absence until it does come in."

"But I was here last year," I repeated. *Does he think I'm not me?* Kyle could easily vouch for me if he was here, but conveniently, he wasn't.

Brandon shrugged. "You still gotta take a temporary leave of absence, I'm afraid."

Fuck you.

Fuck *you*.

I smiled with the delicacy of a grenade. "Thank you."

Brandon returned the gesture, but his was as if he had something to be proud of. It's not like he'd believe someone who not only had a perfect track record here but was, ridiculously enough, acting as a human telephone between Gardiner and Lake.

I didn't feel like I had the power or authority to fight this. If I took this any further, it'd be the same issue magnified ten times, and I didn't want that. To play it safe, I had to play nice. I felt like if I had any chance of getting the best possible outcome, I would need to listen, conform, and comply. I was good at that, despite how much it took out of me. All I wanted—what I'd longed for for *nine months*—was to return to Yellowstone, and even that was at stake.

Since Sanchez had been covering me for the past twenty minutes, I would need to track him down, thank him excessively, offer to buy him a beer or three later, and then apologetically explain that he would need to continue to cover my shift, as well as his, for the rest of the day and probably the next two. I could already picture his naturally cheery disposition melting from his face and mirroring my silent rage. After that, I'd need to head back to the housekeeping office to tell the managers (since, you know, HR was too busy to call them about it) before asking my mom to drop sixty bucks on shipping.

I admit, part of this was my fault. I should have double-checked my shit before leaving the house, and I was furious at myself for it. But blame falls on two shoulders, the other being the HR people who said I was forgiven for it.

All I could do now was do was call my mom.

*   *   *

I was lying on my bed, still in my housekeeping uniform, staring at the ceiling, thinking about everything. No one was here. Not my new, random roommate and not my two new suitemates. Just me.

After what felt like a long time, I sat up and texted Dorian. He was supposed to be coming in tomorrow and I'd been giving him updates over the past few days, so he'd know what to expect coming in. He was my last hope for consistency—everything else seemed to have fallen through.

I wasn't quite ready to talk to him about the HR issue yet. If anything, I wanted to get my mind off of it completely. So texted him, *Take your time getting here because I spent my first day working till eight o'clock lol.*

Lying back on my bed and staring back up at the ceiling again, awaiting his response, I started thinking about what would happen if I actually did have to leave. What was I going to do if I went back home? All of this would have been for nothing. The travel time, the money, my new camping supplies, it would all go down the drain. What would I have back home if I didn't have this? I couldn't relive the past year again.

I felt abandoned by my friends and betrayed by Tyler from last season. I got into my very first wreck and totaled my car in the middle of January and had to walk a mile to and from campus every day. Four months later, I pooled together some money to buy my grandma's Buick off of her. My parents sold our family home of twenty years to a new family and moved into a tiny little apartment down the road, awaiting the next house. I never came home from college because for two weeks over Christmas Break, I slept on the floor and lived out of my duffel bag.

My phone vibrated next to my hip.

Are you kidding me, Dorian texted back.

I started typing out my next response when a follow-up message bubbled through. *Why the hell did I leave England for this lol.*

Despite my terrible mental state, I couldn't help but laugh a little. I backspaced my original message to modify it. *It can only go up from here.*

I clicked the little blue send arrow on my screen before remembering the news he recently shared with me about getting accepted to law school. I quickly added, *Hey, we'll need to celebrate your acceptance into UPenn at the pub when you get here, too! I'll buy.*

He immediately replied. *HELL YES. The Finer Things Club is BACK.*

I clicked my phone off and fell back onto my bed to stare at the ceiling. My mood settled back into what it was before—angry, frustrated, and exasperated. I couldn't help but spiral as the weight of my responsibilities began creeping back up in the silence of my room, like vines on a rotting building.

My mission now was to survive.

CHAPTER 21

·· ◆ ◆ ◆ ◆ ··

HR finally called.

In the little back office, Brandon was sitting there at this desk wearing his same pedophilic mustache and purple puffer vest. I gave the open door a light knock when I stepped in. He looked up and gestured me to one of the metal chairs across from him.

"Hey, Lauren, come on in and have a seat," he said while typing something into the keyboard. I walked over, greeting him with a short *hi* as I sat in one of the two chairs, like a troubled kid in front of her principal.

What could I possibly have done this time? I wondered.

Brandon turned his attention to some papers on the other side of the desk and paged through them until he found the ones he wanted. "So I called you in here to give you an update on your social security card." He paused, watching my reaction before continuing. "We called Gardiner's Human Resources yesterday to get an update on your employment status and they confirmed that they had given you a pass for this season. They sent their records over, which was proof enough to show that you're valid, in addition to your mom's scanned copy she sent over. That being said, you're in the clear. You'll be able to return to work tomorrow. Or even today if you wanted."

I stared at him for a few seconds, confused, while I processed this information. "But...what about FedEx? My mom shipped my card three days ago. She spent, like, sixty bucks on that just to get it here on time." It was still in transit too, and I was supposed to tell her when I received it.

"We would be more than happy to reimburse her for the shipment charges."

I shook my head, ignoring his request. "She mostly just wanted to know if you got her email or not since it's pretty sensitive information. You still haven't confirmed that for her."

Brandon nodded. "I understand. I'll send her an email after our meeting, confirming that I got it. I apologize for the inconvenience, and we'll be sure to pay you for your time off these past few days."

He looked almost...embarrassed. Wilted. Defeated.

It'd be great if you could compensate Sanchez for all the work he had to do on my behalf, too, I thought, irritated with the strain he forced me to put on him.

I felt a little better leaving the trailer but remained a little aggravated at the fact that Brandon didn't believe me when I was telling him the truth in the first place. He could've called Human Resources up in Gardiner that *same* day, but no. He made me wait, take a leave of absence, and place extra strain on my already small housekeeping team, all while forcing my mom to pay a healthy copay for a UPS package containing one of my most sensitive legal papers.

But something about watching Brandon shrink down into himself as he admitted all that gave me a sense of power over him—like I was finally "believable" enough. I liked watching him squirm uncomfortably in his chair and tell me he was sorry. I had credit with him now. He owed me.

I looked down to give a quick glance at my watch and noticed it was already twelve-fifteen. Deciding to skip Brandon's offer to return back to work since I was still irritated and the day was almost half over, I headed over to the Employee Dining Room, despite the lunch rush crowd, knowing I'd be hungry later if I didn't.

Sophia was already there sitting at a window table with Skylar, who was in her kitchen uniform, toque and all, when I walked in with my tray. Pulling a spare chair up to the little table, I asked, "Cool if I sit here?"

They both looked over and smiled, mouths full of fettuccine.

"Hey! Yeah, go for it," Skylar mumbled through her pasta. "Actually, I've gotta get going in a minute anyway, so you can just take my spot."

I frowned. "No, no, you're still eating! It's really not a big deal. I've already got a chair, anyway."

"No, seriously, you can have it. See? I'm already getting up to dump my tray," she said, stacking used napkins and her cup on top of her tray before standing up. "See you guys!"

I finally took her chair, then gave my attention to Sophia, who had asked just a second ago, "Any word?" referring to my situation with HR.

"Yeah," I said, rolling my eyes. "He basically said I was right without admitting it and was going to pay me for my time off."

Her face twisted up. "Well, that was stupid. It's the least he could've done, though."

"No kidding. He basically repeated everything that I told him the first time, which was super annoying. But it's done now, and I can finally go back to work. Anyway, how's your day been?" I asked with a sigh.

She gestured toward the lake, which you could partially see through a window on the other side of the cafeteria. "Pretty good. Walked around the lake for a while and took some pictures. By the way, I was thinking, we should go hiking soon. I haven't gone yet and the weather's starting to get nice enough that maybe some of the snow's melted on a couple of the nearby trails."

Shoveling a fork full of terrible canned pineapple into my mouth, I concurred. "We could go this weekend before your ACMNP stuff starts up. Maybe we could do Storm Point or something, that's a good one. It's fairly short but has these big boulders you can climb on top of to see the lake."

I learned early on that Sophia was also a part of A Christian Ministry in the National Park. She wasn't super dedicated to it, initially signing up with the intention of making friends more quickly. From what interactions she's had with those members, though, she didn't seem to click right away with many of them, so it was mostly just the two of us, plus Skylar on occasion, that hung out together.

"I'd love that!" she exclaimed. "We can take more pictures and walk around and maybe grab coffee or something beforehand from the deli."

"Yeah, that sounds great! I was actually gonna say that we could grab breakfast from here before heading out, but the coffee here's pretty bad," I said, motioning to the section of the cafeteria where the drinks and condiments were. That was when I saw the familiar back of a dark, curly-haired guy wearing a Patagonia hat.

He was sitting at a nearby table, chatting with someone I didn't recognize. My stomach fluttered as I recognized the person from last season who I hiked with, worked with, and shared a campfire at the Grand Tetons with. I looked back at Sophia, pretending not to notice.

Dorian was here.

I didn't know why I felt nervous about seeing him again, despite all texts we'd sent back and forth to each other over the past few days. Maybe it was because we just hadn't seen each other for so long. It wasn't until I heard his smooth, baritone voice ten minutes later that I realized he had suddenly approached my table with Sophia.

"Hey," he said, a foot from our table.

I looked up from my conversation with Sophia to see his face, warm and familiar, along with a brand-new scruff he must've grown between now and last fall. His eyes crinkled on the sides like candy wrappers.

"Oh my God!" I exclaimed, suddenly truly happy to see him. I stood up to pull him into a tight embrace, ignoring the mixture of both surprised and confused faces now looking in our direction from the other tables around us. "You're here! You came!"

Pulling away, I noticed his smile was even bigger now, stretching the widest I'd ever seen it. "It's so great to be here, dude," he grinned. Then he took a step back, remembering he had another person behind him. "By the way, this is Adam, my new roommate."

Objectively, he was very attractive—honey-brown skin and a tall, angular face. I grinned at him like I'd known him for more than the two seconds I actually had. "Hey, Adam, I'm Lauren," I chimed, shaking his hand. "This is Sophia, my suitemate," I said, turning to her.

"Hi, nice to meet you," they each said to each other, shaking hands.

Dorian's eyebrows then scrunched together, "Hey, wait a minute, what about Candice?"

"She flaked," I said, cavalier about it now. "Texted me just a few days ago, as I was coming in, and said she found someone else to room with. Some girl named Emmy. Then I got assigned to a girl from the Philippines for like five minutes before *she* made friends with another girl from Thailand, so now they're rooming together."

"What the hell?" He chuckled with a funny look across his face. "So you don't have a roommate at all yet?"

I shook my head, laughing with him. "No, so actually, Soph and I were thinking about rooming together now. Skylar, our other suitemate, is probably going to transfer over Mammoth, up north."

"Why?"

"Family stuff going on, I think. Wants to be closer to the exit in case something comes up."

"Ah. That's really lame, though, about Candice. I can't believe she did that to you; you guys had talked about it and everything," Dorian said.

"Yeah, it was a weird start to the season, and that's not even half of it. Remind me to tell you about the HR thing later, you'll lose your shit after you hear what happened."

He groaned. "Ugh, anything with HR makes me lose my shit. Speaking of which, we should probably head back. We've got orientation today." Dorian rolled his eyes as he said *orientation.*

I smiled. "I got lucky! Claire pulled me out early so I could help with staffing—another thing for me to tell you."

"Yes, I wanna hear all the updates! Some of us wanted to go to the pub tonight anyway, so swing by the room later and we can talk shit on Terrego. Pelican 105," he smiled mischievously.

Of course, he would already have a collection of friends— why wouldn't he? He could snap his fingers and already have a posse of hikers ready to go.

"Sounds fab. Have fuuun," I teased in a singsong voice. Waving him and Adam both goodbye, I returned my attention back to Sophia, who had already taken her seat and was poking around at the remnants of food on her tray.

"Sorry, didn't mean to leave you hanging. It was just a bit of a surprise to suddenly see him across the room," I explained.

She waved her hand with a smile. "Oh, no biggie. I would've done the same probably. So that was who?"

"Dorian. He and I worked together last year in housekeeping. He was an inspector."

She nodded. "Cool. Other guy was kinda cute, too."

"Yeah, he was," I agreed, recognizing his features without feeling any particular sort of attraction to him. "I forgot, did you say that you had someone back home?"

She nodded again. "Yeah, his name's Noah. Actually, I've been meaning to call him. I'll probably do it later today; he's been wanting to check in with me and make sure everything's going okay."

"Is everything?"

She shrugged. "Yeah. Thinking about changing to the deli, though."

"Oh yeah?"

"Oh yeah. Have you *seen* my hands? They're the rawest they've ever been from all the dishwashing!" She dropped her fork to pull all her tangly brunette hair up onto the top of her head while she spoke, securing it with a silky, patterned scrunchie around her wrist. "The kitchen sucks."

"Oh," I concluded after peering over to her side of the table to see her hands. They were pretty cracked and red. "Wow, yeah, you should definitely switch."

She laughed. "I need to put some more lotion on them. Actually, I'm probably gonna head back to the dorms. I've been meaning to write some letters to a few people. You ready to go?"

I nodded. "Ready."

*   *   *

I knocked on Dorian's door that night and heard a few muffled voices inside. A few seconds later, he opened the door and gestured me in.

"Hey!" he said, answering the door from his bed. Walking in, I noticed the foot of his bedframe nearly touch the frame of the door, giving him easy access to the doorknob. Across from him, on the other side of the room by the window, was another twin bed where Adam was, lounging with an acoustic guitar. Another guy, blond and skinny, was sitting on something that looked like a tall, wooden box—almost like a crate.

For mid-May, it was definitely humid in their room. It also smelled a little like a musky gym bag, even though none of them appeared to have worked out. It reminded me of how my guy friends' dorm last year in college smelled. I attributed it to a natural dude odor that came with any and every kind of dorm room.

"Hey, how's it going?" I said, locating a spot on the floor near the other blond guy I didn't recognize at the front of the room.

"Um, do you want a chair?" Dorian looked concerned as I took my seat on the receding green carpet.

I pretzel-crossed my legs and leaned against a large wooden dresser. "Nah, I'm good. I can make myself comfortable just about anywhere."

"Looks like somebody got some sun today!" Adam joked. I had no idea what he was talking about until I remembered I had just taken a hot shower and took note of my puffy, red face in the mirror before leaving.

"Oh!" I chuckled, pressing a palm against my face. "Yeah, no, I took a shower right before coming over, so it's probably from that." Combined with that, the heat of the room, and the sweatshirt I was wearing, I felt like I was boiling. It didn't take long for me to also become aware of the small trace of moisture forming along my hairline, so I eventually stripped down to my t-shirt for ventilation.

"So, tell us about Terrego," Dorian said, getting comfy on his bed, like a schoolgirl at a sleepover wanting to know who you had a crush on in class. "What'd they fuck up?"

"Well, it was actually HR," I said, cracking a smile. "But you know Brandon?"

"The new guy with the creepy mustache?"

"Yeah," I said, surprised he knew who I was referring to. "Well, when I checked in back at Gardiner, I forgot my social security card, but they let me pass through because I was a returner and already in the system and shit. So literally on one of my first days of work, Brandon calls me in, and I have to give all of my rooms to Sanchez."

"Jesus."

"Right? I felt so bad. So, he basically told me I had three days to get my card to them, meaning my mom would have to shell out a bunch of cash for overnight shipping, after I had already explained to them that Gardiner said it was cool. Anyway, he ended up temporarily suspending me and by the third day, he called me in again and was like, 'We called Gardiner up and they did confirm the situation, so you can go back to work now and we'll pay you for your trouble.'" I made a makeshift phone with my hand and held it up to my ear as I impersonated Brandon.

Dorian was speechless, along with the two other guys who'd been listening. "Bro," he finally said. "That's fucking *bullshit*."

"That's ass, man," the skinny, blond guy said.

"What a joke," Adam added.

"I can't believe they did that to you," Dorian said, shaking his head. "What a waste of time and money. They definitely should've just called up there themselves to check."

"I know, that's exactly what I was trying to tell him," I answered, exasperated and worked up all over again. "He said they were going to call him, but I guess it took them a while to get around to actually doing it, so I ended up getting caught in the middle of it. But anyway, it's over now and life is wonderful, and I get to unclog toilets again."

He laughed. "Speaking of which, when you texted me about that eight o'clock work night, I almost shit myself. Like, I was honestly so scared to come back."

"Sorry." I winced a little. "Probably should've kept that a secret until you started."

"Probably," he chuckled.

A spell of silence followed. I looked around the room, glancing at their wall decor of multi-colored flags and posters when I took note, once again, of Adam's guitar leaning on the bed next to him and the blond guys' box he was sitting on.

"Wait," I finally said, looking between them. "Were you guys playing music earlier?"

They both shrugged.

"Yeah," Adam answered, "I was playing guitar and Josh over here was doing percussion. You wanna hear something?"

"Of course!" I beamed.

Adam scooted toward the edge of his bed with a half-smile on his tanned face, then put one of his Chaco-sandaled feet on the floor while the other crossed over to rest on his knee. He began strumming the opening chords to "Smells Like Teen Spirit" by Nirvana. To my surprise, the blond guy, Josh, reached down and started hitting different points on the box, making various drum pitches.

As they both began settling into the rhythm, initially off-beat but now a fully synchronized duo, it was like being a part of a mini recording session. They played and played for the next twenty minutes with Adam eventually transitioning into some of his own songs that he'd written. There was one I really liked about a spaceship going to the moon, so he sang that twice.

"What's that thing?" I asked afterward, pointing to the box.

"It's a cajon," Josh said. "You hit different points on it for different sounds."

"He let me try it a couple of times. It slaps. No pun intended," Adam smiled.

Dorian scooted up from the head of his bed where two of the walls formed a corner to sit on the edge of his bed, facing us. "Hey, when do you guys wanna head over to the pub?"

"We can go now," Adam said, putting his guitar back on his bed and standing up.

"And you're finally old enough now to publicly drink!" Dorian chimed.

"Finally!" I grinned.

Laughing, we got ourselves together and headed out.

CHAPTER 22

······◆◆◆······

By June, my tiny, close-knit friend group with Dorian, Adam, and Josh had grown significantly. There were now ten of us and counting instead of the original three—something I wasn't entirely on board with.

Among that group was Cole, a guy who started sitting with us at our table in the EDR for lunch and dinner. He had a strong, athletic build with sandy blond hair that fell across his forehead in a very appealing way. He's an accountant but sure didn't act like one—he wasn't boring and dry. He mostly joked with Adam and Dorian and told a lot of stories about his pre-Yellowstone adventures.

One of the other new guys in the group nicknamed "Stretch" because of his height, who was especially quirky and eclectic, was in the middle of teaching us how to properly enunciate cuss words in sign language. Apparently, this was something he was evidently fluent in. Everyone's trays were pushed into the middle of the table and the EDR was jam-packed for the dinner rush.

"Okay, so this is how you say *bitch*," he instructed over the white noise of the crowd. Tucking his thumb into his palm, as if making a rigid version of the number four, he struck the inner edge of his index finger against his chin. "Bitch."

"That's hilarious!" someone said.

Grinning, all of us began imitating him, saying it back and forth to each other at the table.

"And that's not to be confused with *bastard*," he continued, flicking it onto his forehead this time.

As if on cue, all of us brought our hands higher onto our faces, issuing profanities at each other.

"How did you say *party* again?" someone else asked, leaning over the table to see him better.

"Like this." Making the shaka sign with both hands, he swung them back and forth in front of his chest, so they moved together like two synchronized pendulums.

That same person leaned back, chuckling to himself and shaking his head. "I love that one."

Dinner was starting to wrap up as people started shuffling away and dumping their trays, moving like clockwork.

Everyone laughed and giggled over Stretch's dirty words and the motions that went with them as we shuffled out in a line toward the exit. Once outside, I noticed Dorian step away from the group to walk with me in the back as we returned to the dorms. "I can't believe they put you in the hotel, dude. We would've crushed it in the cabins," he said.

"Ugh, tell me about it," I groaned. "It's okay though, really, I like the feeling of Danica breathing down my neck."

He laughed. "Hey, by the way, Sam from last season, one of the other inspectors, texted me saying she and Tyler were thinking of coming up for the Fourth of July this summer. Maybe we could go camping like we did at the Tetons."

I felt my stomach drop, unprepared to hear his name. I struggled to think of what to say. Watching my shoes as they shuffled against the gravel, I mumbled some half-hearted answer. "Sure, yeah, that'd be cool."

He paused, looking at me. "What, you don't want them to?"

"No, no. I mean, they can, I just, um…" I really wasn't sure if I should tell him or not. It made me uncomfortable just thinking about it. What's a quick excuse I could think of? "It's just…"

Dorian continued to stare at me, clueless and expectant. My face was growing hotter by the second, just thinking about the words I was going to say to him.

I glanced over at the lake, hoping it would somehow offer me the right words to say, before returning my gaze back to my shoes. "I don't—like, I'm not sure how to…"

It's okay, I thought to myself, *you can tell him.*

I lowered my voice enough so that only he could hear me. "Tyler would sexually harass me a lot last summer."

What I didn't dare tell him was how, when we were… "together"—whatever that meant—Tyler would kiss me so hard that my skin would get chapped and I'd have to rub lip balm on it. He would attempt to give me hickeys I didn't want. He would tug at my clothing and whisper suggestions in my ear that alarmed me. He would thrust the back of my underwear upward and turn it into a makeshift thong, revealing my backside, even though I didn't want that. And whenever I said no to a request in that soft, meek way of mine (often smiling while doing so because I didn't want to upset him), he would attempt to seduce me into agreement, which never worked.

What I also didn't dare tell him was how, one time at the EDR, we were grabbing lunch and when I realized I had a rip in my back pocket. Instead of helping me hide it as I made my way out of the cafeteria, or offering me a sweater or something to tie around my waist, he commented, "Damn, those jeans couldn't handle that ass."

And what I also didn't tell him was how when we texted and video chatted back home, he would play mind games with me and make me feel less than. He sent me a picture he'd swiped from the internet showing only four fingers on his left hand and insisted he'd gotten an amputation after a major accident. Foolishly, I believed him, and it wasn't until three weeks later he revealed that he had a bet going with his friends to see how long he could lead me on with that prank.

When he stopped talking to me all together, dropping me for reasons unknown, I turned inward and began digesting everything I was feeling. It was November and I hadn't felt right for months. Something felt askew inside, like I was somehow off balance. That was when I questioned if I was ever sexually assaulted by him, teary-eyed at the thought of that. I decided I wasn't because, technically, nothing *did* happen. Whatever was going on, I didn't feel like I could complain about it since I had agreed to be his partner. I still didn't feel right, though, and I wasn't sure why.

I told my mom about it, who was a mental health therapist. She felt terrible about it, awful as a mother, and knew this was something that I needed to process. She suggested I write out in my journal everything I really wanted to say to him—what I would tell him if I had the chance.

I wrote three very angry letters. I would've sent one of them to him had I known his address. Inside me was a storm of humiliation, embarrassment, and shame. Thick, black clouds swirled under my skin, outraged at the damage and hurt he had caused me—how he had selfishly taken advantage of my inexperience.

Soon after, I couldn't help but slump into a depression. Between him, my first car crash, the loss of my childhood home, and feeling abandoned by my hometown friends, it was all I could do not to tear my skin off and replace it with another body.

I was *miserable*.

By February, three months since the start of my swirl, I was all out of anger. I'd used it all up on hypothetical letters and copious late-night journal entries by candlelight in the corner of my dark room, spilling my guts out in black ink onto the safe, white pages. When I had nothing left to offer but a smidgeon of forgiveness, I drafted a virtual letter to him over Facebook.

I told him how disappointed in him I was, how I wished he could become the person I knew he wanted to be. He wasn't ever proud of himself, never thought of himself as a good person—I remember him saying that to me—but he still had time, I told him. I cherished our friendship in Yellowstone, but now I had no reason to stay connected with him because of his actions against me. I was going to move on with my life and leave him to his, intending to close him out of my life forever. I maintained that promise for two years until one, day, he reached out to me with an apology over Instagram, expressing how sorry he was for the pain he had caused me.

Dorian had stopped dead in his tracks, speechless. "*Whoa*," he finally said. "Dude, that's *not* okay," he said, eyes serious and level, shadowed by the thick furrow of his brows. "That's it, then. We're not inviting them. They're not coming."

"No, no, no, it's okay," I said, shaking my head, "I'm strong, I can handle it. I've healed as much as I could, so as long as I have you or Sophia there with me, I should be okay."

The rest of the group was much farther ahead of us now, active in their own conversations and merriment.

Dorian started walking again as we neared the little two-lane road we'd need to cross to return to the dorm. "I mean, it's your call. If I were you, I'd cancel the whole thing, but I'm standing with you on this. I'll support you all the way with whatever you decide."

Unable to fully look at him, feeling both awkward and grateful, I muttered a simple "thanks."

When the group dispersed upon getting to the dorms, I went with Dorian to his room where he wanted me to help him craft the text he'd be sending back to Sam about the plans for the Fourth of July. We sat on his bed where I watched him type up the bones of what I thought was a well-written text. He spoke every word out loud, frequently leaning the screen over toward me so I could read it over for myself and correct him on any phrasing. In fifteen minutes, we had constructed a healthy paragraph, vaguely explaining how a situation had gone down between me and Tyler, which made me uncomfortable with seeing him again. We hoped she would understand.

Already, I was feeling much, *much* better about everything, thanks to Dorian's immediate support. I was entirely grateful to have someone like him to rely on, who believed me instantly without making me feel like I needed to explain my truth. My stomach unclenched, my jaw relaxed, my heartbeat slowed, and I finally felt like I was free of Tyler.

Sam's reply came through the next day, and she accused us of bailing on them. For the next few weeks after that, she occasionally write comments on my social media posts with variations of, "Glad to see you're having so much fun out there."

They never came.

CHAPTER 23

—·····◆◆◆·····—

I had my first full team today—four people. My usual area of
the hotel was the second floor of the east wing, which meant
I did a lot of running up and down the stairs for supplies
whenever we ran out. Staff could only use the elevators when
carrying crates of dishes, like coffee mugs and spoons.

One of the people on my team was the Filipino girl who
was my roommate for five minutes before transferring to live
with a Thai girl. She was also in housekeeping and was quickly
becoming known as one of the fastest and most immaculate
with her work, which would really help with our pace today.

I was pleasantly surprised to find also on my team Milo,
with whom I worked last summer. He was Columbian with
tan skin and dark hair. He wasn't very tall, maybe around five
feet or so, and had a bit of a flair to him.

"Milo!" I sang, genuinely happy to see him again. "I didn't
know you came back, it's so good to see you again!"

His face lit up when he recognized me. "Lauren!" he
greeted in a thick, South American accent, giving me two
quick kisses on my cheeks before embracing me. Despite his
small frame, the force of his hug was enough for my breath to
momentarily catch in my throat. "Are you an inspector this

season?" he asked, pulling away and letting his hands fall to hold mine, like we were the dearest of friends.

"Yes, I actually just started a few weeks ago," I nodded.

"You are going to be *such* a good inspector," he said. "You were always so nice to work with."

I beamed at him, unable to stop myself from revealing a wide smile. "Thank you! I'm excited to have you on as a room attendant today. If there's anything you need today, Milo, just let me know."

But before letting me go, he patted one of my hands and leaned in as he spoke. "*Please*," he said, charming me with his deep brown eyes, "call me Mimi."

The rest of the morning was going according to plan. While everyone was pushing their carts around (actual carts, not mule carts like the cabins) and risking accidentally waking sleeping guests in the name of housekeeping, I went around checking for more empty rooms and stripping the beds for them to make things move faster.

By lunchtime, we had about ten rooms done, the majority of them already inspected and ready to go. A little less than half of my master list was completed. I knew from housekeeping, though, that the real work started during the second half of the day. Everyone was gone by then, leaving even more rooms open for cleaning and sprucing than on the morning shift. Some RAs moved faster than others, which meant that in addition to cleaning their own prescribed rooms, they'd need to support the others with theirs if they fell behind. The front desk would be radioing me, inquiring about the status of certain rooms, and I'd have to make sure they were cleaned and inspected.

The speed at which I stripped beds increased, the speed at which I replenished supplies—or what supplies we had left—increased, and the speed at which I asked for a status update from my RAs also increased. I was hoping the Linen Truck Drivers, or LTDs, would come by during my lunch break to restock towels and king bed sheets but disappointedly, though unsurprisingly, they didn't.

I grabbed my walkie from my hip. "Inspector Lauren to Lake Hotel LTD."

A brief silence followed before another voice crackled through. "Go for Lake LTD."

"What's your twenty?"

A couple then approached me in the hallway as I attempted to balance a walkie and small stack of bedsheets in my hand. "Excuse me," they said, "we were wondering where we could get more of those cute little bear soaps we found in our rooms?"

My walkie suddenly sounded with a crackled response buzzing through, but it was completely inaudible, as if whoever was speaking into it had it right up to their mouth.

I quickly grabbed it, still balancing bedsheets in my other hand, and managed to say, with minor strain, "Standby," before clicking it onto my front pocket again.

"Try checking with Milo, one of our housekeepers down there. He should have some and if not, try the girl behind him with the dark hair," I smiled as best I could, pointing down the hallway with my free hand.

They nodded their thanks and I returned to my radio again. "Inspector Lauren to Lake Hotel LTD, can you repeat that?"

"About thirty minutes. We're at the Lodge cabins right now restocking," a deep voice sputtered through again.

I groaned to myself. "Ten-four, thank you."

Nearly forty-five minutes had passed and there was still no sign of the LTDs. *Where the hell are they?* I wondered. Now, for every room update I got, they came with asterisks: 231 and 235 were done, but they both need towels. 201 was good to go but needed washcloths. 217 was all ready but didn't have any spoons for the coffee mugs.

So now, not only was I running around trying to locate supplies we didn't have, but I was falling behind on my inspection list. Five new rooms needed my attention, but the others couldn't get done until I gave the RAs what they needed to complete the rest. My throat was dry from all my huffing and puffing up and down the stairs and my feet screamed, but I couldn't allow myself to notice. My mind felt completely frazzled, but it was my job to maintain control. Mid-afternoon was, chronically, the worst part of the day.

Before I knew it, it was four-thirty, when all the rooms were *supposed* to be done but never were. My ex-roommate was working at maximum speed while attempting to maintain her quality of work, Milo was working as well as he could on his first day back, just trying to keep up, and the two others were managing well enough, but could be doing better.

From my hip, I heard a female voice call through on my walkie. "Claire to second floor Lake Hotel inspector."

I dreaded answering. Unclipping it from my pocket, I held it up to my mouth. "Go for Lauren."

"Lauren, can you give me a status update on 214?"

I paused to check my list, releasing my index finger from the radio to run it down the rows of rooms on my clipboard. The box was empty. I could feel the angst beginning to seep into my stomach. "That room hasn't been serviced yet, but I'll run over to get it started."

Claire didn't say anything for a minute. I thought she might've clicked off without giving me notice until I heard her come through again. "What about 221?"

I checked. "That room hasn't been serviced either, but I can send one of my RAs over when they're done."

She went quiet again for a minute or so. "Ten-four. Would you be able to give me a call from the phone in one of the rooms? My extension's 2234."

"Ten-four."

My heart was pounding. I had no idea was she was going to say. What did she want to talk to me about? I thought we were doing well, I felt like we didn't fall behind until now, but anyone could say that about any of our teams, mid-afternoon.

Keying myself into a room I knew was vacant, I propped the door open by shoving a blue rag from my back pocket under it—a practice that was against regulation but everyone did because doorstops were hard to come by. Then I dialed her number from the room's phone with shaky fingers. The dial tone rang twice before Claire answered.

"Hey, Lauren."

"Hi."

"I thought this would be a more private way to talk, but I wanted to let you know that I'm sending Inspector Kendall from cabins over to help you out. They're almost all done over there, so whatever RAs are free, they'll be coming over to your wing. What rooms do you have done?"

I read off a modest list of inspected rooms that had been fully completed since lunch and attempted to mention the ones that had been serviced but were needing final supplies.

"Okay," she said, taking a deep breath. "Lauren, I know this is tough for you, but I need you to just manhandle the group. Instead of stripping beds and gathering supplies, all I want you to do is just inspect. Kendall's going to help you do that, but in the meantime, it's literally just all hands on deck, okay?"

I nodded. "Okay, thank you."

I felt like crying. I thought I was doing my job. I know I was, at least to the best of my ability. I still hadn't received any kind of formal training, just critiques from my managers as they passed by. At the same time though, I was falling behind on room inspections—I had six or seven I still needed to get to—and had to admit that maybe a little support was needed. But I knew my RAs would slow down if I didn't help secure their needed supplies. I chose to sacrifice my own efficiency to support my team, four people whose job it was to clean, vacuum, dust, organize, and replenish in no more than forty-five minutes. I could do mine in ten. I figured getting them what they needed was more important so they could focus on cleaning and not waste time looking for materials we did or didn't have. I made that my responsibility.

Management, however, wanted me to prioritize my job, something as simple as inspecting, over my housekeepers'. Yet, at the same time, it felt like they had also issued a punch in the gut by telling me I wasn't even doing my job.

Inspector Kendall arrived when the LTDs did. She took a look at my list with me, and we decided to split all the uninspected rooms in half. When she finished her half, she would help with acquiring more supplies for the housekeepers. Meanwhile, the two linen guys—an older, rounder, scruffier guy and a much younger, skinnier guy—were taking their sweet time stacking sheets and towels in the storage room down the hallway.

The rest of the RAs showed up toward the end and in less than an hour, everything was finished. Danica came up to take a look around and make sure everything was in its proper place. Expecting a simple "nice job", she instead critiqued, "Blue bags aren't supposed to be placed around any of the fire extinguishers. It's a safety hazard, so you guys'll need to move them."

I felt like chucking rocks at her.

When the RAs finally finished and I'd inspected their carts, I decided to draw silly doodles on their papers next to my signature as a token of my appreciation for their hard work. One was a flower, two of them were suns, and at another's request, a bison, which looked more like a severely disproportional horse.

When they left, after some of them took the recycling bags, trash bags, and dirty dishes away, I rounded up a few extra stray towels to throw into one of the large LTD laundry bins by the stairs.

"Are you married?" the older LTD suddenly asked me, just as I was about to head downstairs. He was working nearby and was heavy set with a gruff voice and wore the kind of glasses that tinted in the sunlight. His lenses were still somewhat black as he looked at me, having just walked up the stairs from his truck to bring in more bedsheets.

I looked around to see who he was talking to. The other LTD, the younger, skinnier guy, wasn't nearby. I wasn't sure why I was looking for him. Maybe as a buffer or something.

"Am I...married?" I repeated.

"Yeah. 'Cause ya got a ring on your finger." He motioned with his head to my hand.

I looked down. Not sure which one he was referring to, I looked at both of them, one on my left middle finger and one on my right index. Both of my ring fingers were bare.

Holding up my left hand so he could see my empty ring finger, I answered, still confused, "No."

He nodded as he picked up a blue bag to dump into the nearby bin to take back up north to be laundered. "I was just wonderin'."

Turning around to leave, I heard him call out to me once more.

"Hey, you want a CD?"

I looked back at him, waiting for him to further explain, but he didn't. "Do I want a CD?" I repeated again.

"Yeah, I made one. They're in a little box over there." He gestured with his head toward the stairs where there was a little open-topped cardboard box, before grabbing another plump, blue trash bag of towels to dump into the bin.

Peering inside, there must've been fifty copies of the same disc. It had a dark green background with wispy, paint-brushed strokes of color, yellow, red, and blue. In the top left corner, it said in white letters, "Murphy Miller: Going Back to Missoula."

"Sure," I finally said, thinking it'd be rude if I rejected his offer. He didn't say anything after that, just continuing to dump bags of linens into his bin.

After crossing the hotel and running up to the housekeeping office to return my key, I hastened outside a little faster than normal, desperate for the open air. I began the dusty, gravel walk back to my dorm, fumbling around with my string of earbuds when I heard a familiar voice call out my name. I turned around to see Dorian behind me.

"Hey," I said, stopping to wait for him and pull out the earbud I had just plugged in.

"Did you hear?" he said, pulling a green square out from his jacket pocket with an overly genuine smile. "Murphy's a closet music artist."

I let out a laugh, feeling mine in my pocket too. "I heard he's got some bangers on there, like 'Going Back to Missoula.' Did he also ask if you were married?"

His face scrunched up, both amused and taken aback. "Did he what?"

I held up both my hands. "He asked if I was married when I was dumping some extra towels into the bin. They're not even on the right fingers," I laughed, turning my hands back around to look at them again for myself.

"Oh, Murphy," he lamented, rolling his eyes. "What a character."

"Well you know what they say," I said.

"What?"

"Work hard, play...music," I joked, stumbling around with my words.

Dorian let out a big laugh. "Yellowstone really is a piece of work."

CHAPTER 24

·· ◆ ◆ ◆ ·· ──────

Today was actually moving at a decent pace. In fact, it was good enough that we might be able to get off early enough for—oh, I don't know—say, a Fishing Bridge milkshake. One of the first times I had one was last season with Gretchen and Sarah at the little diner inside the gift shop, and I wanted to relive that. Maybe they tasted so good because there was no other place to get a milkshake. Maybe it tastes better after a full day of working or hiking. Whatever it was, it worked.

It was Dorian's idea to grab one with a few people after work. "Hey," he called out from down the road. We were both scheduled to work together out in the cabins today, him covering the five hundreds and me covering the six hundreds. I was outside one of the many canary-yellow houses when he called out.

"What do you think about grabbing a milkshake from Fishing Bridge with a few people after work? I have a feeling we'll be finishing before they close," he added.

"Sure!" I called back, walking closer to him so I could hear him more clearly. "I thought they closed at like eight, though?" I said in a normal voice.

He shook his head. "Changed it. They close at five-thirty now."

My eyes popped out of my head. "Five-*thirty?*"

"Five-thirty. So, we'll need to book it. But I think we'll make it just in time, just as long as management doesn't detain us for something stupid, like cleaning doorknobs," he said, referring to last season.

"Ugh, don't remind me," I said, rolling my eyes. "Sounds good though. I'd *love* a milkshake. Haven't gotten to have one yet!"

"Me either," he said with a smile, "but we're gonna today. We're gonna make it happen. I'll text the rest of the group and see who'd be available to come too and we'll make a thing of it."

Our group had expanded so much that one of our people decided to create a GroupMe for easier communication. In total, it had thirteen people, including Dorian and me. So now, anytime anyone wanted to do something or go somewhere, we put it in the group chat since everyone operated on so many different work schedules—housekeepers, valets, cooks, seating hosts, waiters, deli workers, dockhands, you name it.

Since I knew the cabins like the back of my hand, I was able to make more progress on inspecting my list of rooms. Only one of my four RAs had a really long list, so I had the first finisher help him out while the others finished cleaning theirs later that afternoon. Dorian sent me some of his free workers, too, before calling the hotel to see if they needed help.

He sent only two out of his four RAs to other parts of the hotel and told the rest to check in with management. Once my team finished up not long after, I grabbed my radio to check in with everyone else, like Dorian.

"Inspector Lauren to all Lake Hotel inspectors, does anyone need RA support?"

Silence fell for a few seconds before a few responses began sputtering through.

"Nope."

"Negative."

"No thank—"

"Yes, in the east wing on the second floor."

I recognized that last person's voice. I didn't know her very well, but she was always trying to hog RAs for herself and probably already had a whole team helping her out between the people at the hotel that were already there and anyone else who had checked in with management about where else they were needed. Instead, I sent one her way and told the two others to head back up to sort the bags of recycling they'd accumulated throughout the day after they restocked their bins.

Mindful of the time, five o'clock, I ran up the massive hill toward the hotel and up the stairs, where I practically threw myself through the door of the second-floor housekeeping office. My goal was to update them on rooms as quickly as possible, hand in my key, then scram. I still needed to change, find out where everyone was meeting, and have enough time to make the ten-minute drive north to Fishing Bridge for milkshakes.

Upon entering, I found Danica, the assistant manager, sitting inside with her office door wide open. I was expecting to see Claire, the head manager with her piercing blue eyes, since she'd been around for the majority of the week, but I knew that, with Danica sitting in there, things would be anything but straightforward.

"Lauren!" she sang before I barely even stepped into her office. She was already looking at me through the door frame with that big smile of hers. "How's it goin'?"

Taking a few seconds to catch my breath, I answered, "Pretty good, just wanting to check in. Everyone on my team's been signed off and they're taking care of recycling downstairs now."

She nodded, turning her attention to the computer monitor and beginning to type across the keyboard. "Awesome. Well, I think we're all caught up around here, but I haven't seen anyone from your team come by yet to turn in their lists. So in the meantime, if you just wanna kind of hang out here until they come by, that'd be great."

What? This was a first. I'd never heard anything before today about waiting for an entire team of housekeepers to finish before an inspector checked out. I mean, I guess it made sense, but if there was nothing for me to do and everyone was wrapping up anyway, why keep me?

Anxiety heightened now, I nodded while avoiding eye contact. She was playing big sister and wanted me to know that she was in charge since Claire wasn't here.

Sitting in one open chair right outside, I waited like a school kid by their principal's office. My leg began bouncing up and down with nerves and all I could do was wish for time to slow down. The clock on the wall read five-ten—twenty minutes till closing. At a loss for what to do, I fished my phone out of my front pants pocket and texted Dorian.

Danica is holding me captive.

What?? he replied no more than a minute later.

Yeah. Said that since I'm the inspector, I would need to wait for my team to check out first.

Are you kidding? What is she having you do, just sit there?

YES.

That's bullshit, he said, *I've never heard of that before.*

Me either. I really want this milkshake, dude. It's literally all I have to look forward to rn.

We're gonna make it, he promised.

Five minutes later, at five-fifteen, two of my RAs came waltzing through the door, chatting like old pals. They passed by me and into Danica's office with a quizzical look, something I desperately wished I could explain away. But I couldn't. I had to sit, silently, and wait for one more.

Ten minutes left.

By this point, my leg was bobbing uncontrollably. I couldn't stop it. My palms began to sweat as my frustration grew. It was all I could do not to clench my fists and let my nails dig into the center of my hands.

The main door of the housekeeping office squeaked open, and I craned my neck enough to see around to the other side of the door. It was the third and final person on my team. I smiled tightly at them and watched them saunter over to the office. All Danica would need to do is look at his list for my signature and tell him that he could go home. That's *it*.

Minutes after my last RA had been cleared, Danica popped her head out with a smile that was just a little too sweet for me. "You're good to go, Lauren. Thank you."

Dashing out of there like a mad dog, I whipped out my phone and shot a quick, three-letter text over to Dorian. *Omw!!*

Thank fucking God, he answered. *Meet us in the parking lot by Pelican.*

I briefly wondered why Dorian wasn't detained, but it could've been because the other assistant manager was there. Pushing this from my mind, I ran toward the dorms, my black drawstring back slapping against my lower back and the loose legs of my black trousers flapping against the wind.

I was *getting* my milkshake.

Just as he said, everyone was in the parking lot, but it was much smaller group than I anticipated—only two of the other eleven group members showed up. Waving at them from the entrance of the employee entrance out by the main road, they waved back and motioned me over to Dorian's light blue Honda, which was easy to spot.

Just as the engine began to turn over, I dove into the backseat of the car like a runaway, gulping in heaps of air like some oxygen-deprived, milkshake-obsessed housekeeping lunatic. I was still in my uniform when Dorian ripped out of the parking lot and sped down the street toward Grand Loop Road, the car's wheels issuing faint squeals while doing so.

Once on the main road, the guys who'd decided to tag along kept shooting me these amusing looks, chuckling to themselves while watching me recover from my crazy, wild-woman state. I opened my mouth to explain what happened but one of them spoke before I could even make a sound.

"Don't worry. Dorian already clued us in."

I nodded, grateful for this. "Thank you."

Without the need to explain anything further, we rolled down the windows and let in the cool rush of the early summer air and aromatic pines. Even though we were in a rush, some small sliver of this moment grounded me and made me feel just a bit lighter.

The familiar shape of the Fishing Bridge General Store peered over the horizon as we made our way closer to it, and I could already taste the first drop of my thick, chocolate milkshake hitting my tongue. Luckily, we managed to find a parking spot almost center of the store in the front row.

I checked my watch as we scurried in, making our way toward the diner in the back of the wide store, most of us still in our work uniforms.

We made it with five minutes to spare.

*   *   *

After Fishing Bridge, we made our way back to Lake to hang out in one of the guys' rooms—Cole's, actually. He said in the GroupMe chat that he wanted a milkshake, so part of the reason we came over was to drop it off for him. His dorm was much newer than ours; it was a single room, painted a warm off-white color, and even had *baseboards*. The dark carpet was plush and not nearly as treaded down as Pelican's or Osprey's. Since he was an accountant for Lake, though, as a part of Terrego, I guess that meant he got perks with his living quarters.

Most of the guys were sitting on the bed or one of Cole's chairs, while I sat on the floor, which I didn't mind. Something about lounging around in a room full of guys made me feel powerful and exclusive, like I was the only female with an inside glance into their world. I tried to laugh and comment just enough so that I would seem social but not annoying, especially for Cole. They allowed me to listen to them talk in the way guys do, which, eventually, boiled down to girls, politics, and sports, until Dorian suggested we go to the pub tonight.

"I even brought back a UK version of Cards Against Humanity we could play, too."

"UK version...?" Cole repeated, confused.

"I studied abroad in Sussex last year," he said. "Snagged the game before I left."

Cole nodded, obviously impressed. "Nice."

Another guy from the group piped up. "I'd love to hit up the pub! Just don't invite Cole. He's got cooties."

Cole laughed. It sounded strong and confident. "I was gonna be over there tonight anyway 'cause there's a ping-pong tournament I signed up for."

"Okay, well, let's pregame for a while at Club Dorian and then we'll text the group to see if anyone else wants to come," Dorian said, referring to his dorm where everyone had been meeting up for pretty much every outing now. It had become the group's default location.

One of the other guys perked up. "I wanna go to Club Dorian."

"Bouncer says you're always welcome," he chimed.

After that, the conversation took a turn toward who would be playing whom tonight on some game they all wanted to catch at the pub. For twenty minutes, they discussed who was playing, who sucked the most, what their streaks were, blah, blah, blah. I tried to keep up with them and extract something from their talk that I could maybe contribute toward but, unsurprisingly, came up empty. Around that point, I was left more and more to my thoughts, feeling excluded all over again.

Part of me wanted to leave, but the other part didn't so I could at least stay in the room with them. I was conflicted between my desire to leave so I could be in my own element somewhere else and the potential of the conversation in case it turned toward something more interesting that I could contribute to, especially so I could impress Cole.

I decided to text Sophia. I knew she'd be around if she wasn't talking to her boyfriend back in Georgia. It seemed he always called, always wanted to check in with her and make sure she was safe, and every time, while rolling her eyes, she would work to convince him that she was.

Boys are dumb, I said.

Her message bubbled through a few minutes later. *Tell me about it. What's going on?*

I let my fingers fly, ignoring everyone around me in the room. *First of all, as much as I love being around Dorian, he didn't leave me alone the entire way over to Cole's dorm. I tried to put some distance between us so no one would think I was interested in him, but I couldn't shake him.*

I told Soph about my attraction to Cole pretty much from the start of Yellowstone. She and Skylar both knew about it, but nobody else. I never knew what to do when I liked someone—I always got really quiet, played it like everything was normal, and ignored pretty much every opportunity to make progress. Being attracted to Cole felt intimidating and I wasn't quite sure why. Maybe because it was so new and I hadn't really dated anyone before. Luckily, I knew Soph and Skylar both had my back and would help me only when I had the courage to ask for it. In the meantime, they both stayed quiet about it with me.

That's really annoying, I'm sorry. Who else have you been talking to there?

Well that's the thing, I wrote back, *it's all dumb shit. It was girls and now it's sports, and I feel ignored.* I sent that message, then immediately had a follow-up thought that I began hammering out: *It's so funny bc you and I talked about everything under the sun a couple days ago over coffee for 2 hours in the sunroom and now I'm here listening to them talk about Duke versus KU's basketball teams. :/*

A wall of blue covered my phone, indicating my long paragraphs of text. I watched her bubble her response in a little gray icon on the bottom of my screen before her message finally popped through.

Lol RIGHT. That's why I'm so glad I have you to talk to about that stuff haha. Maybe they're trying to impress you or something. Just leave if you're not having fun, she wrote.

I thought about it. That's what I'd always done before. It was my rule of thumb—if I'm not having fun, leave. It was risking a reaction from the group that always worried me. I didn't want to have to explain my leaving.

I might. Probably will.

Sitting on the floor, I had to remind myself that I was in a room full of young men. I didn't want to listen to them anymore because all I knew was that I felt ignored. If I left right now, I could go back to Soph and spend some time with her before she went in to work at the deli tonight. Together, we could talk about anything we wanted to. More *interesting* things.

"I'm gonna head back. I'll see you guys at the pub later," I finally said, standing up from my pretzeled seat on the ground.

A couple of their faces looked confused, but for the most part, they didn't seem to mind.

"Okay, see ya later," Dorian said, indicating my leaving wasn't a big deal. "My room, eight o'clock."

I nodded, then turned around and left.

CHAPTER 25

·····◆◆◆·····

Not so long ago, Sophia switched from being Skylar's roommate to being mine, mostly because Skylar had originally intended to transfer to Mammoth, up north, to be closer to family. In the end, she decided to stay here, though I wasn't sure why. Maybe something worked out, maybe whatever was going on in her world had passed, I don't know. Soph and I were excited to know she'd be living out the remainder of the summer with us, but something still wasn't right. Something was off. The usually bubbly and kind Skylar had become quiet and soft-spoken. She smiled less and looked more tired, even cried at lunch today, and no one knew why.

When Soph and I both got off work at roughly the same time, we devised a plan to help Skylar feel better; we would visit the first-floor vending machine and dump ten dollars' worth of our tip money into it to buy as much junk food as we could—Reese's, M&Ms, Pop Tarts, Twix, Cheetos, Chex Mix, and potato chips. Then we'd display it all on her bed for her with a Welcome-Home-We-Love-You note while she was away at work.

We didn't know how much time we had to work with, so we had to hustle. Juggling the secret snackage in our arms and shirts, we hustled back up the stairs to our room on the second floor, passed through the shared bathroom, and peeked through the crack in Skylar's door to make sure no one was there. It looked like her new roommate, another friend of our large group, wasn't anywhere to be found either, which meant we had the whole room to ourselves.

"The coast is clear," I whispered to Soph, who was standing behind me with an armful of colorful plastic bags and wrappers.

We tip-toed over to Skylar's bed to dump all the snacks onto her already-made bed and started organizing them in a giant collection on her pillow. Soph placed all the chips, the largest bags, in the back and I did the candy bars farther down, working together to create an arrangement that descended in size. Soph was just about to place the note we had written earlier in the very front to complete the colorful assembly when we suddenly heard the doorknob start to jiggle.

We shot each other a panicked look and scurried back into our room, shoving each other through our doorframe on the other side right when Skylar walked in, catching a glimpse of us at the last minute. Soph and I couldn't help but start cracking up as we fell to the floor of our room in a frenzied defeat. Our plan had just barely been foiled.

Skylar ran in a few seconds later with both hands over her heart, her dark, voluminous hair bouncing all around her as she did so. "You guys!" she grinned, unsure of whether to laugh or cry. "This was the nicest thing anyone's ever done for me!"

Neither Sophia nor I could formulate words, just sounds as our stomachs cramped with laughter and a damp band of sweat collected around our hairlines and the elastics of our bras. The room had quickly grown very warm in the midst of our running, huffing, and snorting. Skylar couldn't do anything but laugh with us, and before we knew it, the three of us were sprawled around on the floor desperate to catch our breaths.

"We were trying to surprise you, but we heard the door handle turning and started running away!" Sophia managed, after propping herself up on her elbow.

"Well, I heard some rustling around inside, then I saw you guys running away and thought you were just trying to borrow something! It wouldn't have been a big deal if you were. I just would've been like, 'It's okay, you don't have to sneak off with it or anything!'" Skylar grinned.

This was the first time I think any of us had belly-laughed in a while and it felt good. Skylar had been unhappy, I had been feeling left out, Soph had been constantly reassuring her boyfriend of her safety and warding off flirting guys in the kitchen at work, and we all just needed to feel something good. It was too easy to get caught up in the drama and imbalances of the park.

We stayed on the floor talking for a while, making ourselves comfortable on the old, disintegrating carpet floor of the dorm. There, Skylar explained that something had happened to a friend of hers that she knew from high school. Something tragic and irreversible. The details of it weren't worth going deeper into, but we all knew what she was alluding to. So, we just sat there with her in the middle of our room, hoping that would be enough.

"This was the nicest thing anyone's ever done for me," she whispered after a bit of silence, tears brimming her eyes.

"We're in this together," I reassured her, before we all embraced one another on the floor of our dorm.

CHAPTER 26

‧‧◆◆◆‧‧

I remember the first time I consciously tried to make friends with a boy. I was in third grade and always wondered why girls always had female friends but never the opposite. I'd seen plenty of movies and TV shows where there was always a main character with two best friends, one of whom was a boy. I really didn't see any reason why I shouldn't have one or why having one would be weird. So, one day, a kid named Logan whom I sort of knew started talking to me and I let the conversation carry on naturally. He was a little odd and people made fun of him because he had a pet rat, but I didn't think that was too big of a deal.

We were lining up in alphabetical order at the front of the classroom to leave for our next activity, and Logan's last name happened to come right after mine, so he stood behind me. He and a couple of nearby friends and I started chatting as we waited for the line to get moving when Logan randomly placed both his hands on my shoulders in an affectionate way. At first, I didn't even notice because I was so engrossed in chatter with one of my friends. Suddenly, one of them pointed at him and said, "Ew, Logan's touching her!"

I turned around to face him, feeling his hands drop back to his sides. He looked ashamed and embarrassed, and I wished I could've made that go away. At the same time, though, I wondered what would've compelled him to do something like that. It didn't take long to figure out—he had a crush on me. I knew it even before deciding to be friends with him, but I thought that wouldn't mean anything when it came to being friends; I thought I could just ignore it and have things go on like normal without anything weird happening. I took a risk, and I was wrong.

That was among the first times I learned to stick with girl friends because I knew they wouldn't try anything. They wouldn't flirt with me or try to touch me. They would just talk to me, the only thing I ever wanted.

The now larger-than-ever friend group, which, coincidentally, consisted mostly of guys, decided to spend the evening at Butte Point, a lookout point with a fantastic view of the lake, about twenty minutes from the dorms. There must have been a forest fire not too long before that left all the trees bare because even though we were nearing July, the stems were tall, charred veins of bark standing lifeless and bent. But beyond them was a vast blue pool of lake water that you could watch from the very top of the hill we had driven to.

Three of the four parked cars were ours. Between the thirteen of us, we brought eight hammocks, three books, seven beers, and one speaker for music. It was an atmosphere I'd hardly known with others, despite my college age where in theory I would have had ample bonfires, parties, and get-togethers. This was a new experience for me in that it was much more communal; people didn't flirt with people, we just shared space together. We were a group, a team. Most of us brought something the others didn't have—I borrowed Adam's extra hammock straps, Stretch borrowed my blanket, and we all took turns swapping playlists to play through the speaker.

In a lot of ways, I felt like I was at home.

Half the group was wearing brown, Aztec-patterned pullovers, a trend that Skylar and her roommate, Elle, unintentionally started a couple weeks ago. Everyone loved them so much that they went out to the gennies to drop over forty bucks on their own. It was Dorian's idea to call them jerseys.

"You guys bought them?" asked Derrick, one of our older members in his late twenties who originally immigrated from El Salvador, as we were walking up the hill to find a good hammocking spot.

Two other people I wasn't as close with in the group nodded and paused to show off their brand-new jerseys they'd just bought. "Yeah, we got them today at the gennie in Fishing Bridge."

"Well damn, I need to get one now," said Adam, Dorian's roommate, who was beginning to look much tanner now that summer weather was finally rolling in.

Derrick from El Salvador turned to me. "Lauren, I'm surprised you don't have one yet." We were next to each other in the middle of the group as we walked up the large hill from the parking lot onto a trail that led to the top of a nearby peak where we could get a better hammocking view.

I smiled. "Yeah, it's on my list though. Waiting to get paid before getting one, but I'm planning to this weekend!"

"Me too. I was gonna buy mine today after I heard we'd be coming to Butte Point, but I didn't get off work till later."

As he spoke, he took his hand out of his pocket and reached over to hold mine, not even looking at me—more just doing it as a casual action, as if we'd held hands before.

I laughed, looking down and taking my hand out of his. "Derrick, what're you doing?"

He shrugged. "Nothing. Are you offended?"

"No."

"What happened?" one of the girls asked, turning around.

"He reached over to hold my hand," I said, feeling both confused and amused.

Dorian looked over. "Hey man, aren't you dating Elle?"

During a few of the times that Skylar came over to Sophia's and my room, she mentioned that her roommate, Elle, and Derrick were seeing each other for a bit. A couple of days ago, she mentioned they had recently broken it off and wanted to remain friends. I guess things were just getting a little too complicated between the two of them.

"Nah, not anymore," he said, tucking his hand back into his pocket.

This wasn't the first time Derrick had done something like that. He'd occasionally reach over to feel a strand of my hair for reasons I didn't understand. Each time, I'd ask him about it, but he wouldn't ever really offer an explanation. I decided it was just another quirk of his.

"Hey guys, does this work?" Adam spoke up from the front of the pack, looking back at us. We'd stopped at an area among the charred trees open enough to give a nearly clear view of the lake, but close together enough that we could easily string multiple hammocks between them without too much hassle.

Everyone nodded in affirmation and started setting up their stations, some people lounging two to a hammock. One of the members started playing easy-listening music through the speaker, and it didn't take long for us all to settle into our elements. The younger, skinnier LTD guy who worked with creepy, homemade CD–making Curtis, was lounging with one leg dangling outside his hammock and a cigar in his mouth, laughing at something someone must've said. Dorian was to my right, swigging a beer with his clubmasters on, sharing his hammock with Derrick, who was reading. Adam, Dorian's roommate, was finalizing his hammock by tightening his straps around a massive tree trunk. Some of the girls were clustered together taking photos of each other, and Stretch was advertising his world-famous back massages in sign language on a fallen tree trunk.

Eventually, paperback books by John Muir and Henry David Thoreau made their appearances. This was something I noticed early about Yellowstone. Instead of tabloids and clickbait, people here read poetry and journal entries by philosophers and explorers over a century ago. It was because of our environment; you can't compare the richness and vastness of a national park to something as simple and cheap as a tabloid magazine or click baited YouTube video. You *had* to be expansive and open yourself up to the environment that surrounded you, which often provoked large questions about life, ourselves, and our futures.

I knew that this moment was something special. We had all traveled here to put ourselves in the way of beauty, and here it was, staring us back in the face as a reflection of our own actions.

"What are you reading?"

I looked over to see Derrick peeking over at my book. He was sitting across his hammock, so he rested upright while his feet dangled above the grass.

I held it up for him to see. "*The Prophet* by Kahlil Gibran. It's this really dense poetry that puts the philosophies of different stuff into metaphors, like money, friendship, houses, and time."

"Is it any good?" he asked.

"I mean, *I* think so." I shrugged. "But it's sort of like really rich food, you know? You have to take it in small doses to really enjoy it. What are you reading?" I asked, leaning forward to see what he had.

Derrick held his copy up while keeping his thumb inside, securing his place. The cover read: *The Divine Dance: The Trinity and Your Transformation* by Richard Rohr with Mike Morrell.

"It's really good," he said. "It's mostly about creating this modern vision of God and experiencing it in a more approachable and accessible way. It's probably one of the best books I've read on this sort of topic. Here, take a look."

After he dog-eared his page, we swapped books to get a closer look and explore each other's annotations in the margins and paragraphs of the texts. Next to a large paragraph, he had scribbled in jagged font, "Oh, how good is this!"

I didn't know what to say. "Wow," I managed. "That is some seriously deep stuff."

"It really is. I like yours, too. It's definitely philosophical. You know I studied philosophy and theology in college, right?"

I was surprised. "Really?"

"Yeah. Graduated in it and everything."

I saw out of the corner of my eye a tall, lanky figure heading our way through the clusters of tall grass and rock. Turning, I saw it was Max who worked with the LTD Curis. Derrick greeted him as he made his way up the hill. "Hey, man."

"Hey," he chimed, taking his cigar out of his mouth to chat. "I heard you guys talking about books and thought I'd join the conversation."

I didn't know Max very well, but I got the sense he was someone who took a casual thing and considered it—studied it—in a silent sort of way. He was the observing, perceptive kind.

"Yeah, we're just talking about philosophy and stuff," I smiled.

"What does...uh...Gibran say about it?" he asked, leaning over at the cover and attempting to pronounce the author's name, skipping over his first entirely.

"Well, let's see..." I said, turning to the section I was on about children. I read a paragraph that explored the balance between raising a child with your thoughts and perceptions as a parent and the child's own individual personality. When I had finished, Max let out a deep, smoky breath.

"Wow," he said, mesmerized. "That's deep, man. You know, if I ever got a girl pregnant, I'd work my *ass* off for my kid. I'd be the best damn dad I could be. I mean, I wouldn't want that to happen, like, tomorrow or anything, you know, but if it ever did, I would be there for both of them the whole way."

Derrick nodded. "Me too. I'd love to be a dad someday."

I smiled, genuinely believing their words, feeling their consideration and dedication. "I think you both would make great dads."

As the temperature began to drop over the next couple hours and James Taylor's "Fire and Rain" came to an end through the speaker, we all prepared to leave, feeling around and shining lights on the ground below our hammocks, checking for any forgotten or hidden items.

That night, when I returned, Sophia was reading in bed with her lamp on.

"Hey," I said, dropping all my stuff on the floor by my bedframe.

"Hey, how was it?" she asked, dog-earing her page and sitting up.

I let out a deep sigh. "It was great. Sorry you couldn't make it; you would've loved it."

"I probably would've," she smiled back. "My creep of a boss at the kitchen wanted me to work later than I thought. Then I had that ACMNP thing afterward. Otherwise, I definitely would've gone."

"Oh yeah, how'd that go? The Christian ministry thing?" She had told me about a bonding event with all the other churchgoers our age in Lake. As she spoke, I started changing into my boxers and sweatshirt, preparing for a long night of talk with Sophia—my favorite thing in the world to do with her.

She shrugged. "It was okay. It's kind of funny, I was actually thinking about how much I don't really resonate with many of them," she said. "It feels like a lot of them are more into it than I am."

"You're a free spirit," I smiled.

She laughed in that wise, colorful way of hers. "I'm a hippie."

I crawled into bed on the other side of the room and for the next several hours, we explored hypotheticals, spirituality, metaphysics, the meanings of meanings, life, and each other, all while lying in bed in the dark, staring at the glow-in-the-dark stars someone before us had stuck onto the ceiling.

"Soph?" I finally asked before dozing off, feeling myself straddling the line between sleep and consciousness.

"Yeah?"

"I think you're the friend I always wanted to have."

I could feel her smiling on the other side of the room. "I think you're the friend I've always wanted to have, too."

CHAPTER 27

······ ◆ ◆ ◆ ······

"The guys want to come over for our movie night tonight," Soph said as she pulled her long, tangled brown hair into a bun on top of her head, securing it with one of her multicolored scrunchies.

She was referring to these two guys, roughly our age, who lived across the hall from us and were roommates. They're more her friends than mine since they all work in the kitchen together. Every guy she meets falls for her; she could name three right now, not including her boyfriend back home. In fact, when one of those guys heard she was sick, they brought a thermos of hot soup to our room just for her.

It wasn't hard to see why they all liked her though—in addition to her free spirit and long hair, she was a glowing, grounded person who had eternally bare feet, flowy bohemian dresses, and flower crowns. She was a mug of hot tea in the fall and a glass of lemonade in the summer. Refreshing.

Micah, one of the two guys coming over later, was a tall and lanky pothead who could never get to work on time and flirted relentlessly with Soph. Jakub, the roommate, was a Slovakian gym-goer and flirted just as much as Micah, though you could never tell if it was just his personality or because he really did like you.

"Okay, that's cool," I said. "What are you in the mood to watch?"

"I don't know," she pondered, "I was thinking maybe *The Secret Life of Walter Mitty*. It's got Ben Stiller in it and that chick you like from SNL."

"Oh, Kristen Wiig?"

"Yeah!"

We'd occasionally go back and forth between movies I'd seen and ones she's seen. Last time, I picked *Casablanca* with Ingrid Bergman and Humphrey Bogart, one of my very favorites, and played it knowing it would potentially become hers too. We watched it on my bed through my laptop, which doubled as a DVD player, buried under a mound of blankets, and ate something called *povitica*, a type of Eastern European sweet bread. My parents started buying it on special occasions from a local place and recently sent me one that was chocolate. I think Soph and I ate nearly half the loaf together that night watching *Casablanca*. Tonight though, we agreed to hide it under my bed so we wouldn't have to share it with the guys when they came over since it was such a delicacy.

"Hey, did you end up switching over to the deli?" I asked, switching into more comfortable clothes.

"No," she said from her bed, "HR isn't letting me transition. Maybe it's because we're already in the middle of the season or because they don't have enough kitchen staff in the Employee Dining Room. I don't know, they didn't really tell me."

"Oh. Well, that sucks," I said. "I'm sorry."

She nodded. "Looks like it'll be more chapped dishwashing hands for me."

"Hey, did you hear about that pub party coming up, though? That might help you take your mind off it—you know, give you something to look forward to."

Soph sat up. "No, but that sounds interesting. When is it?"

I shrugged. "I don't know, sometime next month in July I think. We had one last year—a dance—that was in the rec center, and it was okay. Felt a little like high school for me, so maybe they're switching it up this year. I thought I heard it was going to be a masquerade."

"Really? I'm not gonna wear a mask."

"Me either. I don't even know where you'd go to get one unless they're giving them out there."

"That'd be pretty cool if it fell on my birthday," she said. "Oh yeah, I meant to tell you, my mom sent me like a hundred bucks for us to blow at the dining room in the hotel. Maybe we could dress up and make a big thing of it!"

My eyes widened with excitement. "Really? Oh my God, let's do it! That was super nice of her, too."

Just then, a knock sounded through the closed door. Soph got up to answer it and saw that it was Micah and Jakub through the peep hole. "Hey, what's goin' on, guys?" they said, stepping inside as she opened the door.

"Not much," Soph said, "just hanging out, talking about work stuff."

Micah made a face with his eyes red and droopy. "Ick. Don't remind me. I gotta work tomorrow. Five a.m. shift."

"I think I come in at seven," Soph said.

"That means I'll get to spend my day with you then," he said with a sparkle in his eye.

Jakub walked over and sat on my bed while I stood by the tall, standing dressers near the door. "Don't mind him, he's just stoned," he said in a Slovakian accent. "We got back from hanging out at Canyon today, so he's a little under the influence. I mean, I am too, but at least I'm better at hiding it. Actually, we were thinking about going camping near Avalanche Peak sometime soon if you guys wanna come."

"Oh," Soph said, giving me a look from across the room. "Yeah, okay. We'll think about it."

We were both thinking the same thing: *no.* Soph and I both knew we didn't trust them enough to go camping with them mostly because we already knew what that night would be made of—lots of drugs, alcohol, and lackluster conversation. If we went, we'd be wishing we were back here.

"Good," Jakub said. "Just text Micah if you end up wanting to come. He's checking his phone constantly to see if you texted him back anyway."

Micah was now sitting on my bed, lounging on his bony elbows so his head nearly touched my stack of books and journals on the windowsill behind him. "Shut up, man, you got people you text too."

Jakub chuckled again. "Yeah, but at least I have more self-control than you."

"Touché," Micah replied, leaning back until his head bumped into the stack of content. He turned around to see my window collection of books and journals and picked up my brown leather journal I'd bought a couple of years ago sitting on top of the stack. "What's this?" he asked, glancing my way. "Is this yours?"

My heart began to thump in my chest. "Yeah. It's nothing crazy though, just scribbles. Hey, were you guys gonna do that volleyball tournament next week?" I asked, hoping to change the subject.

Ignoring my comment, he opened it, flipping through the pages like he was at the local library, considering checking it out.

My mind and body froze. I didn't know what to do to make him stop. That particular journal, out of the many I brought with me, was the most sacred. I'd bought it specifically to write down my deepest and truest thoughts—ideas, poetry, hopes, fears, desires. Even Soph hadn't seen it. No one had ever seen it. It was only mine.

And he was *reading it.*

Jakub leaned over toward him to see what it was, and I watched both their eyes scan my writings, pilfering through my words like thieves in a goldmine. I was being held at gunpoint with my own weapon, feeling as though I couldn't make any sudden moves for fear it would kill me.

So I watched.

I internally pleaded, hoping they could hear my silent thoughts, *Stop. Please stop reading my thoughts. Please.*

"These are really good," Micah finally said, looking over at me. He had no idea what he was doing to me right now.

I didn't want to respond, but I felt I had to. It was a compulsion in me to never show negative emotions, to never show I was bothered, to always be nice. I didn't know how to let my guard down; not even for something like this.

"Thanks," I breathed, feeling like I'd been stripped of oxygen.

"*I admire those who stay soft after facing the world in its cold face; daring to believe, with the entire being of their soul, that life is still patiently waiting for them to dance in its light…*" he read from one of my more recent entries.

I could've cried. Those words weren't meant to be spoken, only read and felt. Poetry was delicate and sacred, and hearing Micah, stoned and superficial, read my words aloud felt like he was somehow contaminating them; not even *I* had read my own thoughts aloud. And here he was, taking the liberty of doing it himself for *multiple* people to hear without my consent.

"Why don't you share any of these?" Jakub asked in his accent, looking over at me from across the room.

"I don't know," I said, attempting to keep my voice even, despite the slight tremble in it. I didn't care if they *liked* my thoughts, I cared that they were *reading* them.

"But why?" he pressed.

I was beginning to feel my pain evolve to anger. "Because they're not meant to be read out loud. I've never even let other people read them before," I said, hoping he'd understand what I was trying to say.

I turned to Sophia next to me, my eyes begging her for help. She read me without hesitation and turned her attention back to the guys.

"Well, I'm starting to feel a little tired, so we should call it a night," she said.

"What about the movie?" Jakub asked.

"We'll watch it some other time. I'm starting to feel pretty sleepy. Besides, it's already eleven o'clock. If we start now, it'll be close to one a.m. by the time we finish."

"Oh shit, yeah, and I gotta work at the ass crack of dawn too," Micah said, tossing my little leather journal back onto my bed as he sat up, not bothering to secure the little leather strap back into its groove.

Jakub laughed in a mocking tone. "Ha-ha, I get to sleep in 'cause I got the day off tomorrow."

"Screw you," Micah said, looking at him with his reddened, dazed eyes.

"See you guys later," Jakub said, getting up before closing the door behind him.

When it was silent again and we'd heard their door across the hall shut, I walked over to my bed, placed my journal back on the windowsill where it belonged, clasped shut, and buried myself under the covers, letting the first tear fall.

Sophia walked over, knowing full well why I was crying. "I'm so sorry, Lauren," she said softly, climbing into bed with me. She wrapped her arms around me and held me while I wept.

"They read my journal," I whispered, barely managing to get out the words in the same breath. "They read my journal."

She didn't say anything, just continued to hold me.

Sophia wrote enough to know that when you write at all, you're exposing a highly sensitive area of yourself that is meant to bloom only in the presence of a blank page and nothing else. You're extremely vulnerable when you decide to share a piece with someone, regardless of whether it's a story or stream of consciousness. And seeing Micah and Jakub pick up my pages and begin reading them without consideration for the person they belonged to was like having my thoughts be assaulted.

What hurt the most, though, was how much I wanted them to stop, but didn't—*couldn't*—because they'd stolen my voice.

And ironically, I didn't want to hurt *their* feelings.

*   *   *

I woke up the next morning feeling like death. I was defeated and nonexistent. For a while I just stared up at the ceiling, feeling the weight of the previous night. Glancing over to my left, across the room, I studied Sophia's empty bed. She had left for the morning shift.

On my desk, within my line of sight, was a note with my name on it in Soph's handwriting. I reached over to grab it and pulled it back under the sheets with me and read:

Lauren, I can't tell you how sorry I am about what happened to you last night. They shouldn't have done that to you. If you want, I can talk to Micah about it for you and about how much it actually upset you. I'm always here for you whenever you need to talk. Much love, Soph.

I put it back on my desk and picked up my phone, dialing my mom's phone number. I hoped she wasn't with a client as I listened to the dial tone, suddenly remembering that she was an hour ahead of me.

"Baby girl!" she chirped. "What's goin' on?"

Hearing the sound of her voice made me bawl. "Mom..." I started, not even attempting to disguise the quiver in my voice.

Her tone immediately changed. "What's wrong?"

I explained to her what happened last night and about how much I didn't realize it had destroyed me. Saying all of it out loud made me sound like a baby. *For God's sake, Lauren,* that voice in the back of my head told me, *it's just writing.* "I feel sort of silly about getting upset about all this, but I really don't feel like going to work today," I admitted.

"That's really hard," Mom said on the other line. "I know how much you confide in your journals, and it feels awful having someone just read through them like that. But I think going to work would help you get your mind off things."

"But Mom, I feel *terrible.*"

"What you end up doing is ultimately your decision, but I think going to work would give you something to do instead of ruminating on it."

I gave a heavy sigh. "Okay," I finally said, letting out a dense, heavy breath, "I'll go."

CHAPTER 28

·····◆◆◆·····

"You okay?" Dorian asked.

I shrugged, feeling incapable of lying. "Micah and Jakub read my journal last night."

"Damn, dude," he said, trying to understand the gravity of it even though I know it didn't mean much to him, "that sucks."

"Tell me about it. I feel like shit."

Dorian eyed me. "Yeah, you looked different walking in today. You know what would make you feel better? We should get everyone together tonight and go out stargazing at the tennis courts behind the dorms tonight. We'd been talking about doing it for a while anyway."

"Yeah." I nodded, feeling slightly better. "That sounds good."

We were waiting with the other inspectors and RAs in the conference room. One of our managers would be rolling in soon, most likely Caleb. He was one of our co-workers last summer who worked as a room attendant. He used to wear jean shorts and long, dangly earrings like George Michael, with his wild and wavy hair bouncing about with every stride he took; now he wears khakis and a puffer vest like the rest of the men in management. It was easy to see how much it wore on him compared to last season. Caleb's eyes, formerly bright and lively, were often fatigued with the stress and pressure from his attempts to please both the guests and his supervisors. His posture was slightly slumped as he walked into the conference room behind Claire, our head manager, who rattled off a series of low-priority announcements.

"And remember," she added, "we have those people from the oil company coming, so we'll need to make sure to address all our SPAT rooms first. For those of you who are new, that means 'Special Attention,' and you'll want to clean those first since they're more time-consuming."

I leaned into Dorian, my voice low so Claire wouldn't hear me. "Don't you think it's a little ironic that Terrego hosts those guys?"

He gave a dry chuckle. "Yeah. But it's okay because they're promoting a 'softer footprint,'" he said, holding up one of the many green paper door handle cards from his clipboard.

I leaned back, attempting to hide my smile.

"If you have any other questions, be sure to ask one of us. All right, y'all, I think we're ready for keys," Claire concluded.

Caleb came forward with the usual bucket of keys and began reading off names and tossing them to the respective RAs pooling around the conference table. We had more housekeepers than ever before now that tourism season was in full swing. In fact, there were so many here that there weren't nearly enough seats for them all, so many had to paste themselves up against the walls and stand for the whole meeting.

I wished I was out in the cabins today instead of the hotel. I didn't want to be where people, especially management, could see me. I wanted to work in solitude, listening to my own music with my earbuds jammed in, ignoring everything and everyone around me. I wanted to be allowed the privacy of sulking but prepared myself to work in the public eye anyway.

After our usual post-meeting stretches outside for everyone and their mother to see, I walked down to the far end of the east wing and up the flight of stairs to the second floor. There, I would begin to knock on doors and strip beds for the RAs. My team and I made enough progress until lunchtime, which was typically when all resources would begin to diminish: coffee mugs, spoons, sheets, towels, teas, coffees, and, of course, the Linen Truck Drivers wouldn't get there until an unfashionably late hour.

None of this was ever my fault, but I was conditioned to believe it was. For the next few hours after lunch, I would run around the hotel like a chicken with its head cut off, offering what remaining scraps I could find to my team. And I still couldn't use the elevator.

By three o'clock, not only was the entire hotel centered around rolling out the red carpet for the big oil guys who'd be arriving this afternoon, but I was beginning to fall a little behind on my rooms. Learning my lesson earlier in the season, thanks to Claire's "guidance," I started sweeping through all the empty rooms, inspecting and calling in each of them as quickly as I could. Punching in a specific code with the star key to the in-room telephones would register them as vacant in the front desk's computer system. By doing that, the receptionists wouldn't have to constantly radio us for a status update.

As my RAs began to finish, I called out to the other inspectors on my radio and asked who needed help. "Inspector Lauren to all Lake Hotel inspectors, does anybody need help?"

Voices began to crackle through like they always did.

"Cabins are good."

"Sandpiper's good."

Like always, though, someone requested additional help in the hotel. "We could use some on the second floor of the west wing."

I sent three of my four RAs over in that direction and walked over after checking their carts to support another nearby inspector who needed help on the third floor with a few different rooms. The first was no big deal and, thankfully, had all its needed supplies and amenities. The second room was occupied (which no one had told me), and I managed to walk in on a man in his bathroom taking a nude photo. Erasing that from my mind, I knocked on the door of my third room, calling out "housekeeping" in quick succession to notify any hidden occupants, and walked into something I was not expecting:

No one had cleaned it.

"*Fuck*," I whispered to myself. I popped my head back out into the hallway, hoping one of my RAs was still around, but no one else was out there. It was just me.

I double-checked my list, thinking there must have been a mistake somewhere, that I maybe accidentally marked it off as one room when I meant another. There wasn't.

I looked back up. There was no way I could clean this whole room by myself. It'd take forty-five minutes, at least, and absolutely no one had that kind of time right now.

Danica, with her long, jingly lanyard and sundress, sometimes liked to sweep the halls to check on things in the afternoons. What if she saw me standing here in this dirty room with no one else around? There was a good chance she'd probably make me clean it myself.

Instead, I closed the door.

"Inspector Lauren to all Lake Hotel inspectors," I said into my radio.

I waited for some voices to filter through.

"Go ahead."

"Go ahead."

"Go ahea—"

"Go ahead."

"Does anybody need inspector help?" I asked, attempting to push away any negative thoughts of getting caught. *It's okay,* I thought to myself, *no one's going to be staying in that room tonight if I don't report it. I'll clean it myself first thing tomorrow morning.*

It was quiet for a minute. For a second, I thought I'd be able to finally report to management and clock out for the day until a voice sputtered through.

"Yeah, I could use some help on the second floor of the west wing," he said.

I groaned to myself. "Ten-four," I reported back.

Because there was no connecting floor between the two wings, I hustled down the flight of stairs to the first floor, all the way to the center part of the hotel, past the deli on the left, past the front desk and porter desk, to the main staircase of the hotel, and up the stairs that led to the conference room. Instead of turning where the conference room was, I continued down the hallway, occasionally poking my head into rooms with open doors looking for the inspector covering this section.

Walking deeper into the bowels of the long, carpeted hallway, I heard the familiar sounds of a radio in a nearby room and poked my head in to see Sanchez hastening in and out of the bathroom, mounds of towels and sheets on the floor. Stepping into the frame, I gave a couple quick knocks on the door. "Hey, Sanchez."

He looked up. "Oh, hey, Laur," he said, pausing to check his clipboard. "How's it goin'?"

"Not bad. You staying busy over here?" I teased.

He exhaled his laugh, rolling his eyes at the same time. "Please, I wish I was busier," he joked dryly. "Would you mind inspecting 210 through 216 for me? That'd really help me out."

An aching pain flooded the soles of my feet just hearing those room numbers. "Sure thing. Want me to find you when I'm done?"

"Sure, that works. Thanks, Lauren."

By the end of the day, my master list of all the rooms I'd helped clean and inspect was a disaster. Black scribbles from the many ballpoint pens in my pocket drenched my paper like a neurotic sketch artist. I made my way over to the housekeeping office next door to the conference room in hopes of checking out with whoever was manning the desk inside. Luckily, it was Claire, who was highlighted by her dyed blond hair and mascara-encrusted eyes. Getting out in a straightforward manner would most likely be a breeze.

"Hi," I said, stepping inside to return my key to the little box hanging on the wall.

"Hey, Lauren. Everything go okay today?"

"Yeah, it was really busy."

"I hear that. Oh, I do have some discrepancies to go over with you. Can you tell me the status of 202?"

"Cleaned and inspected."

"214?"

"Cleaned and inspected."

"And 221?"

My breath caught in my throat for a minute. That was the room I had decided to leave for tomorrow. In the short span of time I had to answer, I suddenly found myself saying, without any good reason, "Cleaned and inspected."

Claire pushed a mechanical pencil into the fan bun atop her bleached head after typing everything into the computer. "Thanks. And you already helped out the west wing, right?"

"Yes."

"Great. I think you're good to go then. Thanks, Lauren."

I hurried out of there as quickly as I could, ignoring the immense guilt that had begun to solidify in my chest. What my fate would be tomorrow was a mystery I intended to ignore.

*   *   *

My mom was right. By the beginning of the evening, I had forgotten most of what had occurred less than twenty-four hours before, apart from having something new to feel dread about. Stargazing with the group later tonight felt much more enticing now than it had this morning, so I made my way over to Club Dorian to meet everyone else who'd be coming. I needed to have some fun, mostly because I knew if I didn't, I'd just be in my room lying in bed, reflecting on how envious I was of everyone who was.

The tennis courts we'd be stargazing from were just out the back entrance of our dorm. From Dorian's room, we all made our way out the backdoor just down the hall and sprawled out across the soft, acrylic surface, waiting for the night to deepen. A lot of people brought blankets and snacks with them. Most had changed into some comfortable combination of sweatshirts, sweatpants, or legging. Despite the warm temperatures of the day, it could get pretty chilly at night, as low as the forties. I found myself huddled in a little group with our somewhat recent suitemate, Elle, Sophia, and Derrick.

I mentioned to them the irony of Terrego hosting the big oil guys at the Lake Hotel every year for this annual conference or something they had.

"I heard those guys are jerks," Derrick said. "I don't even work in housekeeping, and I've heard that."

"Me too," said Elle, pushing her long, blonde hair out of the way. "I heard in the dining room kitchen today that they ordered over two hundred dollars' worth of food last year and left like a five-dollar tip for the waitress."

"I thought it was the President of Terrego who did that," I said.

Sophia laughed next to me. "Either way, that's pretty bad."

I grimaced. "And they always invite their lady friends up with them, too. My manager mentioned this morning that some of us would be expected to work late to do turn-down services for them over the next few days. Thankfully, I didn't get picked for that. I wouldn't do it no matter how much overtime they'd pay me."

"People are assholes," Derrick groaned.

"Did I ever tell you about that guest who almost made one of my co-workers cry?" Sophia asked, transitioning from sitting to lying on her stomach.

"No," we said, concerned yet intrigued.

She nodded with her eyes wide as she shifted, getting more comfortable. "Yeah, so she switched over from the kitchen to the deli and she said this woman started chewing her out about how she'd been waiting in line for over half an hour and wanted her food to be free because of it. They had to explain to her, though, that it was the lunch rush, so, obviously, everyone had to wait."

"Did you have to give her the free food?" asked Elle, twisting a strand of hair between her ringed fingers.

Soph shook her head. "No, they had to get their creepy boss to come talk to her since she wouldn't calm down."

Derrick shook his head. "I'm so glad I got out of F and B."

"What's that?" I asked.

"Food and Beverage."

"Yeah, well some of us are still stuck in it," Elle groaned.

"It's amazing how normalized stuff like this is," I said, "and even more amazing how entitled fully grown adults can be. Like ma'am, we're just a bunch of twenty-year-olds trying to do our job."

"Exactly," said Soph. "I mean, at the end of the day, we're just a bunch of college kids trying to make some extra cash."

"Hey, a shooting star!" someone across the court shouted, pointing a finger up at the sky. All of us turned onto our backs and looked up to see if we missed it. I didn't see anything but continued to look for others, determined to find one for myself. Shooting stars had become my silent promises, my special hints that something great was on its way. If I was meant to see one, then I would.

I tuned out the clusters of scattered conversation around me as I focused on the night sky. That same celestial crack in the ether floated above me. I remained on my back, studying its cool, iridescent glow against the indigo backdrop and imagined it was staring back at me. There was too much light pollution back home to ever see the Milky Way Galaxy, so I wanted to absorb it as much as I could while I was here.

I heard a female member of the group, laugh hysterically at something Dorian must've said on the other side of the court.

"Are they a thing?" I asked whoever was listening in our little circle.

"Who, Ari and Dorian?" asked Derrick, clarifying my question. "I don't know, but I heard she's really into him."

"Me too," said Elle. "Actually, I heard a rumor that Dorian planned all this because he was going to ask you out tonight, Lauren."

I jolted up, turning around to look at her, my eyes wide with alarm. "What?"

She propped herself up on an elbow, her blonde hair, longer than mine, swinging behind her back as she did so. "I mean, I don't know for sure, that's just what I heard."

I shook my head, scrunching my eyebrows together. "He was going to ask *me* out tonight?" That couldn't be right. Dorian was my friend. *Only* my friend. That was all I ever wanted with him and now the only guy friend I'd ever truly had was...interested in me.

"Don't act so surprised, Lauren," Derrick said nonchalantly. "I mean everyone knows he's in love with you."

"He's not in love with me."

"It's pretty obvious that he is," Soph agreed, shrugging. "Sorry to tell you."

I couldn't tell whether they were joking or not. I didn't want Dorian to like me. I wanted *Cole* to like me. That had been the goal for the past month and a half; *he* was the one I wanted to have something happen with, even though he was somewhere else in his own separate group on the tennis court.

For the next half hour, I didn't say anything. I remained disengaged, bathing in my own resentment and frustration. I considered getting up and returning to my room where I could seclude myself from everyone, but what good would that do?

Sophia touched my arm. "Are you okay?" she asked in her soft tone.

"No," I said. "I'm mad. It's going to ruin our friendship if Dorian asks me out tonight. I can't let that happen."

"Then stay by me. If we're together, he won't bug you," she said.

I nodded. Soph held my hand and stayed quiet with me after that. Together we watched the stars in our own little bubble of silence, listening to the late-night chatter of everyone else around us. I wished she and I were the only ones out here; we could talk freely about anything we wanted, our thoughts and feelings. We could vent, we could daydream, we could just *be*.

I had yet to even see a shooting star.

Another hour passed before people began to leave. It was close to midnight, and they most likely started to turn in from a combination of fatigue and the chilly night air. It didn't take long for an opportunity to arrive after that because, eventually, only me, Soph, Skylar, and finally Cole remained.

"Well, I'm starting to get tired." Sophia yawned. From the corner of my eye, I saw her nudge Skylar.

"Yeah, me too," she said, yawning. "I gotta work the morning shift tomorrow."

"We'll see you guys tomorrow," Soph said, walking away with Skylar.

Only Cole and I remained.

We sat in silence, still staring at the sky. Despite my chance to say something, I didn't. I wasn't sure what to say to him. This was our first time alone together. He probably didn't know what to say to me either.

"Cole?" I finally asked. My voice sounded like it belonged to somebody else.

"Yeah?"

"Do you like me?"

Silence fell between us. It was deafening. Then...

"Yes."

My eyes stared wide at the black sky, totally surprised. "You do?"

"Yes."

I smiled to myself, praying he couldn't see it.

CHAPTER 29

———— ··•◆◆•·· ————

"Lauren?"

I was in the housekeeping office highlighting my lists for the day when Claire summoned me. Setting my clipboard and markers down on the floor where I was sitting, I got up and tiptoed to the door, careful not to step on anyone else who was on the ground.

"Yeah?"

"Could you close the door?" she asked without looking up.

Suddenly nervous for reasons unknown, I turned around and shut it, hearing the little *click* inside the doorframe.

"One of the rooms you reported back to us yesterday was dirty. No one had cleaned it." Her cold eyes pierced me like a knife. "Max and Murphy, the LTDs, had to do it when they came by to grab bags last night."

I was caught off guard, even though I shouldn't have been, and the thoughts in my head weren't translating into words. All I could make were tiny, inaudible squeaks coming from my throat. "I…"

"Is there anything you want to tell me about that?"

"I…I was afraid that—"

My voice cut out. I could only look to the closed door for help but knew full well that I was the one that had put myself in this situation. Danica's face popped into my head as I tried to speak again, but I stopped myself from saying her name as I turned back around to face Claire, remembering she was right outside the door.

Sensing there must've been a reason behind it, she softened her stare, but continued to press. "It's okay, you can tell me," she said.

My eyes began to feel hot, as if tears were preparing to fall, but I held them back. Instead, it was my voice that fell through, sliding up two octaves higher than normal. The truth came out sounding more like a plea. "I didn't clean the room because I thought Danica was going to make me clean it all on my own. It would've caused a huge delay for everyone."

I didn't say everything I wanted to, not the part about prematurely dismissing my RA who was responsible for it and how I'd intended to clean it first thing this morning. I wouldn't let myself and I didn't know why.

Claire must've thought my explanation was valid enough since neither of us would've put it past Danica to pull something like that. She would comment on your work while you were cleaning, she would issue commands to room attendants that she could do herself, and it wasn't often you received a compliment. Yet she always smiled, remaining bushy-tailed and cheery, as if the whole hotel was in tip-top shape.

Claire nodded her head and dismissed me before returning her attention back to the computer monitor. "Just make sure you're checking all the rooms next time. Okay?"

I nodded. "I will."

And I meant it.

*   *   *

I got back to the room at a decent hour to find Soph on the bed texting her boyfriend, something the poor internet service still allowed us to do.

"Hey, how do I tell Noah that I want him to chill out and stop texting me so much?"

I walked in and threw my bag on the bed, flopping down on my back next to it. "Something like, 'I'm always happy to hear from you, but I need you to trust that I'm safe here with my friends and I'll let you know if something doesn't feel right.'"

"Thanks," Soph said, texting out a version of that response. Throwing it on the bed after she finished, she looked over at me. "You look beat."

"I *am* beat."

"Well if you're up for it, I heard the quartet's supposed to be playing in the sunroom tonight. We could bring our books and just sit and read for a while if you want."

I sighed, feeling my bones release their tension. Soph could read me in a way that no one else could. "That sounds fabulous. I might even get a glass of wine or something. I'll share some of mine with you if you want. You'll be old enough in like a week anyway, that was closer than me when I tried to order something last summer," I said, reflecting on the previous season's scare.

She smiled. "Sounds good."

The sunroom of the hotel, one of our favorite hangout spots, was honeyed in the glow of the sunset. Everything had that warm, yellow hue that made you want to sit in a patch of sunlight on the hardwood floor and take a nap. We had found a spot in the back since all the good seats up front were taken. Elders, families, couples, singles, everyone had their place inside and the two of us sat together, side by side, in a wingback loveseat toward the back reading our novels.

We'd bought our books a couple of weeks ago when we decided to take a spontaneous road trip to Cody, Wyoming, to get out for a while and stock up on snacks. The nearest Walmart was over two hours away, so we decided to make a mini adventure out of it.

It was in the cereal aisle where we both squealed with sheer delight when we could actually scroll through our social media feeds for the first time in months. "It's *so fast!*" we cried over and over, ignoring the confused stares on strangers' faces.

One of the other places we visited afterward was Legends Bookstore, where we each spent the afternoon perusing the aisles and flipping through the pages of books, searching for one to bring home with us. On the way back, a pile of snacks and two new books in the backseat, we headbanged to Soph's new Bollywood playlist downloaded at Walmart down Highway 20 on maximum volume with the windows down.

And here we were, in the sunroom reading those exact books, sipping wine, and basking in a corner patch of sunlight. I was halfway through mine, which happened to be a romance, something I never read. It was one of those light reads you could conquer in about as much time as it took to ship an Amazon package without a Prime membership—three to five days.

As we read, an older couple came in and made their way toward the matching loveseat in front of us, across from a dark wood coffee table. I glanced up from my novel to greet them with my eyes and immediately took note of how well-dressed they were.

"Is this seat taken?" the man asked. He was wearing a button-down with khakis and—believe it or not—an ascot. An *ascot*. The man could've been Ralph Lauren's second cousin for all I knew.

Soph looked up, too, as we both simultaneously answered, "Not at all."

The man and woman both smiled with warmth as they lowered themselves onto the couch. Soph and I went right back to reading but could feel them both watching us. Neither of us said anything until we heard the man's voice again.

"What are you both reading?" he asked, leaning in with the same kind smile as before. It almost matched the sunroom.

Soph paused, sticking her thumb inside to temporarily hold her spot, so she could show them the cover of her book. "*The Death of Mrs. Westaway* by Ruth Ware. It's a mystery."

The man nodded in confirmation, as did the wife who was watching. Then he turned to me next, expectant.

Of all the books I had read in my life, this one had to be my guiltiest pleasure. I could've whipped out *The Alchemist* by Paulo Coelho or the copy of *1984* by George Orwell that I'd borrowed from Skylar. But no. I sheepishly showed him my copy of *How to Find Love in a Coffee Shop* by Veronica Henry.

He nodded as if he was pleased with my answer. Then he asked us a simple question: "Do you both enjoy reading?"

"Yes," we both answered without hesitation, giggling at each other.

"We've been borrowing books from friends, too," I added.

I watched the lady grin along with the man, quiet in a sophisticated way. "You would like *A Gentleman in Moscow* by Amor Towles," he said. "One of the greatest books ever written in my opinion."

"Really?" I asked, intrigued.

"Definitely." His eyes brightened as he scooted toward the edge of his couch to tell us more. "It's a gentleman who's under house arrest in the Metropol Hotel in Moscow during the Russian Revolution. It spans over thirty years of his life, revealing all the people he meets and experiences he has with those people. It's very well done."

Listening to him, I found myself curious about who this man was. Where did he come from? I wanted to use that classic line from *Casablanca* I had grown to love: *Who are you really and what were you before? What did you do and what did you think?*

I whipped out a pen from my bag. "What was the name of it again?"

His eyes crinkled at the corners like caramel candy wrappers as he repeated the title. "*A Gentleman in Moscow*...by Amor Towles." He spoke slowly as I scribbled the title down on the inside cover of my book.

He gave me a few others to consider as well: *The World According to Garp* by John Irving, *The Meditations* by Markus Aurelius, *The Stranger* by Albert Camus, *Heartburn* by Nora Ephron, and *The Cazalet Chronicles* by Elizabeth Jane Howard.

Before I knew it, an entire page had been filled in the back of my book, full of the names of other books.

"Thank you," I said, looking back up at him, laughing a little. "This is a great list."

"Can you text me the names of those when we get back to the room?" asked Soph.

The man looked pleased. Here, in front of him, were two young, well-read women discussing about books and stories, something he obviously had a great passion for, and we were able to share this moment together in the comfort of a warm sunroom.

He and his wife didn't stay much longer. After sitting and enjoying the quartet for a while, they got up and left, but not before saying goodbye.

"Enjoy your books," he nodded. "It was a pleasure to meet you both."

"Same here, it was nice to meet you too," we both chimed back.

And they both left, never to be seen again.

CHAPTER 30

·· ♦ ♦ ·· ─

I'd noticed the group starting to split. It seems it had been for a while, too. Inevitably, both an inner and an outer circle had formed with Dorian the ringleader of the first. He could snap his fingers and make just about anything happen. I was on the outside with some of the others, it felt like.

It became confusing for me, too, because, despite the friends I'd made here this season, I found myself growing resentful toward those in the inner circle who made plans that best aligned with *their* schedules, leaving the rest of us, like me, behind. Although, I mostly talked to some of the guys and my roomies, Sophia and Skylar and didn't mind that at all. They were my group.

I found myself alone in Pelican's lounge room on the ground floor after dinner with most of the group, including Cole, Dorian, and Adam. They were talking about plans for tonight and what they should do. Because I was in a room full of dudes, they all started throwing guyish ideas around, like catching a game at the pub or watching an action movie on DVD in someone's room.

"I've got a better idea," Dorian said. "Why don't we have an exclusive gentleman's night where we dress business casual and walk around the lake smoking cigars?"

The other two considered this.

"I think that sounds great," said Adam.

"Count me in," added Cole. "What about Derrick, though? He'd probably want to come too."

Dorian nodded. "Yeah, probably. We can swing around and grab him from the hotel if he's still doing valet shit."

"We should put it in the group chat to see if anyone else is available," said Adam. "Then whoever wants to come can."

"Yes, good plan," said Dorian. "Actually, we should send out a text to all the guys in a separate chat so none of the girls can tag along."

The guys nodded in agreement and started to talk details. I was beginning to get offended when Dorian turned to offer me an invite.

"You know, you could come if you wanted to," he said. Neither of us brought up anything about that night out stargazing, considering it water under the bridge, whether the other knew that or not. We never did vocalize it.

"Really?" I wasn't even going to attempt to get invited, but I was flattered by his offer anyway. "But that's your guys' thing. I don't want to come and crash the party. Last thing I'd want is to have someone be like, 'Aw man, who invited the chick?'"

He shook his head. "Nah, it really wouldn't be like that. You're chill."

"I am?"

"Yeah. The others wouldn't mind. I know they wouldn't."

I thought about it, really considering it. "Are you sure? Like, I really don't wanna be a vibe killer."

He laughed while Cole and Adam continued to talk. "Honestly, you wouldn't be. Just come meet us at the Lake Lodge around eight. I'll let everyone know you're coming."

I half-smiled, eventually caving into his offer. "Okay. But seriously, text me if anyone's against it. I won't be offended. Should I bring anything?"

"Nope," he said, "we've got it covered."

"All right. I guess I should get ready then. It takes longer for us women, you know?"

Dorian chuckled. "Same here. Gotta look suave as fuck for the finer things club."

"Suave as fuck," I grinned. "Which reminds me! I have stickers for us. I'll bring them tonight."

"Seriously? Oh my God, I can't wait to see them."

"They're pretty badass," I chuckled. "I'll see you later."

After the group disbanded, I walked into my room on the second floor only to remember something very important.

Upon hustling into the room, Soph, who was painting her toenails on her bed, looked over at me, concerned. "What's wrong?" she asked.

Standing in the middle of the doorway, I asked, "Can I borrow a blouse?"

*   *   *

We walked over to the parking lot on the east side of the Lake Lodge, just down the road from the hotel and dorms, where a few of the guys surrounded Cole's hatchback. Tonight, I was wearing my most decent pair of jeans with a white blouse that Soph let me borrow. I even put on earrings. And *mascara*. I hadn't worn mascara in months. My hair wasn't in its usual messy bun either—another phenomenon.

Part of me felt like I was intruding, and the other part felt even more exclusive than I have in my whole life.

"Hey," I said once I reached the general vicinity. They were all peering inside the back of the car, like they were looking for something. "What're you guys doing?"

They straightened up, looking surprised, when they turned around to see me, and I suddenly became self-conscious. *Didn't Dorian tell them I'd be coming?*

"Is it okay that I'm here?" I asked.

"Hey, yeah, no, it's totally cool that you came," Dorian said after a second, stepping aside to make room for me. "We're picking out what cigars we want for tonight."

"Hey, Lauren," Max smiled. I hadn't seen him outside of work since the night we all went hammocking at Butte Point a couple of weeks ago. He had another cigar sticking out of his mouth.

"Max!" I said, pleased to see him and subsequently remembering how he helped clean my dirty room a little while ago. "Oh my God, I meant to tell you how sorry I was about the whole room situation back at the hotel. I still feel so terrible about it."

He swatted his hand at the air in front of him, his smile unbothered. "Ah, don't worry about it, it's no big. Hey, psyched to have you here at our gentlemen's night!"

"Really?" I winced. "I was afraid I'd be crashing the party or something. Dorian said I could come."

"Yeah, dude, you're cool being here," Adam said, bringing a handful of cigars over to me. "Pick one."

I hesitated for a second before diving in and choosing one of the smaller ones.

"Good choice," Max said. "I actually almost picked that one for myself. Need a hand?" He held up the cigar cutter he had in his hand, ready to put it to use.

"No thanks, I got it," I said, taking it from his hand and putting it up against the end of my cigar and squeezing it hard enough until the little brown nub got sliced off. I handed it back to him. "Here you go."

"Wow, you're a fast learner" Max chuckled.

"I've seen my dad do it a few times."

Cole tossed me a little pack of matches from his car. "Here you go. Light up!"

Lit match in hand, I held it up to the cigar and began puffing on the other end, attempting to get the flame to catch. I watched the others do the same with theirs.

When we were all ready, cigars in hand, Cole closed the trunk of his hatchback, and we all began to walk along the margin of the road until we rounded a corner and followed it all the way over to the front of the hotel. Part of the road ran right along a small cliff that dropped down to the cold, blue water of Yellowstone Lake.

We saw Derrick on valet duty from the road, then walked up the U-shaped driveway toward him.

"Derrick!" Dorian called.

No answer.

"Derrick!" he shouted again.

Still no answer.

"*Derrick!*" Dorian, Max, Adam, and Cole yelled collectively.

He turned his head, his face immediately brightened when he saw us. "Hey, guys!" he shouted back in his stiff valet uniform. "What're you doing? You guys goin' somewhere?"

"We're having a gentlemen's night tonight. We tried texting you earlier, but you didn't answer," Cole said.

"Ah shit, I didn't catch that. I'm off in twenty though, can you guys wait for me until then?"

"We'll just be walkin' around. Text us when you're done and we'll meet up!"

"Sounds good!" Derrick peered behind Cole to see me standing behind him. His face twisted into a mix of surprise and amusement. "Hey, Lauren," he said. "You one of the guys tonight?" "Only by invitation," I shrugged.

"Niiiice." His head bobbed as he spoke.

Dorian spoke up. "We'll catch you later man, we're gonna see if a couple other people are around."

"Yeah, sounds good. I think some of them might be back at Pelican."

He sighed. "Fuck. 'Kay, thanks."

As we turned around to make our way back down the driveway and back toward the dorms again, a few of the guys started bugging Dorian about one of the girls in the group.

"You guys goin' out or what?" Adam asked from the front, puffing on his cigar.

"Oh my God, no, we're not," he said, almost sounding annoyed. "Why does everyone keep asking me that?"

"Cause you've been with her, like, constantly," Cole said, his athletic frame more of a shadow against the blue evening sky.

"What about that one chick you hooked up with, that Polish girl?" Max asked, walking next to me. His was much more lanky and wiry.

"What about her?" asked Dorian.

"I don't know, are you still seeing her?" He pulled his cigar out of his mouth and brushed the front of his brown hair out of his eyes with the other hand; it had grown much longer since the start of summer. Everyone's had.

"Not really. She's nuts, man. Actually, I didn't even know until afterward that she has an STD," Dorian admitted.

"Oh, *shit*," Cole said. "You get tested?"

"Not yet, but I mean, you can't get something from doing it in the butt, can you?"

Until now, I had remained quiet and observant, but this was a whole different level. My face scrunched up as my body cringed. "Eww!" I cried.

Dorian flashed me a look over his shoulder. "Hey, you're a guy tonight, remember? You can't say anything."

I continued walking behind Cole, hoping he'd step back and start talking with me, but he didn't. He'd barely made any effort to talk to me after that night at the tennis court, after he admitted he liked me. *Did he lie? Did I incorrectly hear something? No, he did. I know he did. I remembered it. So what was the deal? Maybe I should be the one to make a move. What would I even do? I suck at flirting. Plus, I'm a guy tonight.*

"Three...two...one," I heard Max say next to me.

I turned toward him when I noticed he'd been studying me. "What?" I said, reorienting my focus on him.

"That's what you do when you see someone deep in thought," he said. "You do a countdown and then at the end of it, they're supposed to tell you what they're thinking."

I smiled, chuckling. "Oh, is that how that works?" I said, more as a statement than a question.

He smiled again. "Yeah. So, what's on your mind?"

Wiping Cole from the forefront of my consciousness, I attempted to conjure up a quick lie. "Oh, um…I don't know, mostly just life stuff."

"Like what?"

I shrugged, racking my brain for anything, something false but with the potential to be true. "Like…wanting more out of it, I guess."

He nodded to himself. "I feel that. Anything in particular?"

I liked Max because he asked deeper questions. He really wanted to get to know the subject, whether it be me or a question. "Just wanting to wake up and have life be exactly the way I want it," I said.

Max laughed at that. "Okay, now I definitely get what you mean. I think all of us need something like that."

"Me too." I smiled back at him. It was then I decided to stop trying for Cole. He wasn't contributing toward that feeling.

I hadn't realized we'd already made it to the dorms until we saw Stretch, who taught us sign language back at the start of the season, on the picnic bench by the rickety wooden stairs that led up to Pelican's second floor. You could tell it was him because of the Kramer-like shape of his hair—wild and twisting in every direction.

"Stretch!" Dorian called. "Hey, I thought you were coming with us for the gentlemen's night."

He looked up. Even as the night got darker, you could still see his long, curly hair sticking up in every direction. "Oh, was that tonight?"

"Yeah."

"Oh."

Being back here, I suddenly remembered something I promised myself I wouldn't forget. "Dorian! Hold on a minute, I just remembered our stickers! Do you wanna come up or stay out here?"

"Oh, shit! I wanted to see those! I'll just meet you by the stairs here."

"All right, can you hold this?" I said, giving him my nub of a cigar, the mouthpiece dampened with saliva.

"What sticker?" asked Stretch.

Ignoring him, I raced up the stairs to my room, said a quick hi to Soph, and rummaged through my desk until I found what I was looking for. I huffed back down the stairs where Dorian was waiting at the base, near the picnic bench, for me.

"Okay," I said, pulling my phone out from the back pocket of my jeans to shine the flashlight feature on it. "You ready?"

"Absolutely."

Pointing the light onto the rectangular sticker in my hand, there was a hand-drawn sketch of Theodore Roosevelt I found on Google. The monocle chain he was wearing connected not to a pair of spectacles but to a pair of black aviator sunglasses I photoshopped onto his face. Above his head in archaic newspaper font was written as a boldened heading: *The Finer Things Club.*

"Oh my God..." he said, staring at it. His mouth began to stretch across his face so far that I could see the shadows of his dimples beneath the dark scruff of his beard. "I love it. I *love* it. This is an amazing design, dude, seriously."

Pride filled my chest like helium in a balloon. Dorian was my original Yellowstone person, even if his feelings were stronger for me than mine for him. Our history went further back than anyone else in this group and we always looked out for each other. Tonight was another night spent among the finer things with him.

"Tell me we are it tonight," I said.

"We're it tonight."

CHAPTER 31

· · · ✦ ✦ ✦ · · ·

Tonight was the night Soph and I decided to celebrate her birthday in the hotel's dining room, courtesy of the one hundred dollars her mom contributed toward the event.

Soph wore a new hot pink and sequined bohemian-inspired dress and I borrowed—yet again—another piece of her clothing. We stepped out into the hallway to take my car to the hotel, even though it was no more than a ten-minute walk.

Micah and Jakub, the two roommates who had simultaneous crushes on Soph, were in the hallway talking when we stepped out. Their eyes bulged out of their heads when they saw us. "Whoa," Micah said, eyeing Sophia in particular. "You guys look great."

"Thanks," she said. "We're just heading out to the dining room."

"Oh, really?" he asked. "What for?"

"My birthday," she smiled.

"How old?" Jakub asked, his Slovakian accent coloring his words.

"Twenty-one."

"No way!" exclaimed Jakub, "That's awesome! We need to take you to the pub and get you some shots! Everyone needs to have at least one shot on their birthday!"

She shook her head. "No, thanks. We actually just wanted to keep things a little fancier tonight, so we're dropping a hundred bucks on the dining room."

He gave her a funny look, then turned to me. "Lauren, promise me you'll make her take a shot in the dining room."

"I don't know if they even serve shots," I said.

"So whaddya guys gonna drink?" Micah asked, smelling slightly of marijuana.

"A bottle of champagne," answered Soph.

We got another weird look from both of them, implying that one bottle of champagne between the two of us lightweights would be a bit much.

"Wow," Micha finally said. "Well, sounds great. If you guys need a ride afterward, just call me."

"We will. Actually, would you mind taking a picture of us before we go?" Sophia handed him her phone and we posed against the blank wall of the hallway next to our door, our arms wrapped around each other's waist.

Once we made it to the hotel, we walked as gracefully as we could up the large hill of the U-shaped driveway in our heels to the front entrance. We'd made reservations for seven-thirty because, according to some of our friends who worked in the dining room, the wait staff understandably got crankier and more tired the later you book your evening.

When our waiter came around, once we were seated, Soph instantly recognized him and beamed. "Hey, Antoni! I didn't know you'd be working tonight."

He grinned back at her. "Yes, I got called in last minute. You look wonderful, by the way."

I'd seen Antoni around in the EDR during lunch and dinner. He was maybe seven or eight years older than us (though it was difficult to say with some of the people out here), had a thick Polish accent, and was tall with platinum blond hair slicked back in one of those styles where the sides of his head were shaved.

"What can I get you ladies started off with tonight?" he finally asked, reverting to his professional disposition.

Soph took a quick glance at the menu that had made its way in front of her. "Hm…what do you recommend?"

Antoni leaned over to point to a couple of starter dishes on the "First Course" column of the page. "The Lobster Seafood Ravioli is quite popular right now and so is the Lobster Florentine Dip with the brioche toast for dipping."

We thought it over, considering his lavish, lobster-infused recommendations, but ultimately decided on the seasoned French fries. "Could we also get a bottle of the Michelle Brut?"

"The Michelle Brut? Very good selection," he said, storing all of our orders in his head.

I had no idea if it was, in fact, a very good selection. We mostly just bought it because it was under thirty dollars.

"I'll bring that right out for you. In the meantime, ladies, enjoy yourselves." He walked away, retreating back into the bowels of the kitchen, whose chaos at this time of evening was something I could only imagine.

"We should give him a good tip," I said.

Soph nodded. "We should. He's really nice, too. He used to be in the back of the kitchen washing dishes with me, but transferred here after, like, a week."

"I would, too, if my hands came back looking as chapped as yours. Speaking of kitchen stuff, what looks good to you? I was actually looking at the Poached Pear Salad with the…" I squinted at the menu, "...*tucker aurora cheese*, whatever that is. Or the Alder-Smoked Salmon Chowder."

Sophia grabbed her menu to follow my suggestions. "Ooh, those sound amazing. Actually, the Poached Pear Salad sounds pretty good, too. Or the Montana Wagyu Beef Burger with Butter Poached Lobster. What is 'poached'?"

I shrugged. "I don't know. I've only heard of people doing it with their eggs."

"Have you ever had a poached egg?"

"No."

"Maybe it means fluffy. It sounds like a fluffy word," Soph laughed.

I attempted a quick Google search under the table, waiting nearly six minutes for the first page to load. Finally, I read, "It means 'to cook in simmering liquid.'"

"Oh," Soph said again. Then we laughed. "Sounds like it's basically fried then."

When the champagne and fries came around, we wasted no time. We dug our fingers into the little basket, plunging them into the aioli, while the waiter filled our glasses with the sparkling wine. Then he wrapped the opened bottle in a fancy linen towel before lowering it into a tall, fancy ice bucket in the middle of the table, like it was our centerpiece. Afterward, we gave him our orders and toasted Sophia's birthday with fingers coated in a thin layer of grease and garlic salt.

Before long, we were beginning to feel a slight buzz. We'd only had one glass, but I explained to her that when you mix the altitude with being a lightweight, anything can pack a punch. With that in mind, we slowed our intake and temporarily retreated to our water glasses until the food arrived.

We were quiet for a while, taking in the delicate tastes and aromas of our dishes. The *clanking* and *clinking* of dishes and glasses sounded around us, as did the idle chatter of various couples and families at the other surrounding tables. It was a full house tonight.

Then we began swapping foods with each other, looking left and right before stretching our forks across the table to swipe a taste of the other's entrée, violating a few etiquette rules.

"Mm, that's really good."

"Wow, yours is delicious."

"Oh my God, what's that seasoning?"

"I want to marry your sauce."

By the end of the night, we had finished the entire bottle and most of the food. We were stuffed to the brim, delirious with exquisite satisfaction. *It's a good thing we're wearing dresses,* I thought to myself, *that way, we don't have to unbutton our pants.*

Our waiter returned. "How are we feeling, ladies?"

"Fantastic."

"Phenomenal."

He gave a wide grin with a few nods. "Wonderful. Did we save any room for dessert?"

Soph and I stared at each other across the table. "How much money do we have left?" I asked.

"Twenty dollars."

Tipsy on rich food and thirty-dollar champagne, we agreed to get dessert. "What do you recommend?" Soph asked once again.

"I personally like the Sticky Toffee Pudding. It's a toffee sauce poured over a dollop of whipped cream and sponge cake with chopped dates," he relayed, having memorized it from the menu.

While she thought, I peered down at the menu and took time to think about what I wanted as well.

"I'll give the toffee pudding a go," Soph finally decided. "What do you want, Lauren?"

"I think the Vanilla Bean Brulée Cheesecake sounds amazing. I'll take one of those," I said, looking up at him, doing my best to focus my eyes. How was Soph managing so well? My brain felt like water, sloshing around this way and that with each little motion and thought.

He nodded once. "Very good. I'll get those two items started for you both."

"Thank you," we sang together.

I looked over the table at Soph. "I am literally so happy right now," I said.

She beamed. "Me too! Tonight has been so much fun. Thank you for spending it with me."

"Thank *me*? Thank *you* for choosing to spend it with me. By the way, do you feel anything?" she asked.

"Oh, yeah," she replied, not even trying to fib.

"Me, too. We should steal my coffee pot back from Dorian when we get back to the dorms. I think you're supposed to drink it so you don't get a hangover," I said, unable to remember if that was actually true or not. Last week, Dorian's French press—yes, French press—broke, and he came over to ask if he could borrow mine until his new one came in. We hadn't been using it much lately, so I agreed to let him keep it for a while.

When the bill finally came around, we had topped out at just under a hundred dollars for the entire night. Enough was left over to give our waiter a good tip and pocket five. Trying our best to get up as regular, normal, non-intoxicated human beings, we leveled ourselves as we pushed in our chairs and walked down the main aisle, back into the main lobby and out of the hotel.

"Have a good night, you guys," a woman said from the little desk just outside the French doors of the dining room.

"Thank you, you too," we sang once more.

At the front door of the hotel, I shuffled around in my purse to look for my keys while attempting to balance myself.

"Shouldn't we maybe call Micah?" Soph said.

I paused, thinking about it. "Yeah," I answered, realizing just how uncoordinated I actually was, "that's a better idea." I zipped my purse back up and leaned against the wall while she pulled out her phone to call him.

Micah arrived outside in the circle driveway in about five minutes.

"How'd it go tonight?" he asked as we climbed into his messy backseat. Compared to the interior glow of the lavish dining room, it looked as if both his car and the outside world had a thick, black blanket draped over them. It was nearly impossible to see anything. *What time was it?*

"It was really fun," Sophia said. "We drank a whole bottle of champagne and ordered way too much food."

"So you *did* drink it all," he said from the driver's seat, bobbing his head up and down like he was proud of her for it.

Once home, we thanked him for the ride and made a beeline for Dorian's room for the coffee pot. Standing outside of his door at the end of the first-floor hallway, I gave three quick knocks, not even thinking to check the time in case he was sleeping.

When he opened the door though, he looked wide awake with a mixed expression of surprise and confusion. "Hey," he said, "what's going on? Did you guys go out?"

"Birthday," I blurted out. "Hers. Can we borrow the coffee pot? We don't want a hangover."

Confusion returned to his face. "Yeah, sure, let me go grab it."

When he turned to unhook it from the wall behind him, I noticed a few people from the group hanging out in his room. I wondered why I didn't get notified about it. I was too drunk and too backward to ask about it, though, so after grabbing my coffee pot, I turned around and left.

CHAPTER 32

⋯⋅⋅◆◆◆⋅⋅⋯

The pub was in full swing for the masquerade party, just a handful of weeks before everybody would be leaving for home at the end of the summer.

I never knew how to be a partier. I never really identified as one, but here I was, drinking, sweating, and dancing with a hundred other people in the middle of the pub. I learned to lean into these kinds of social events a little more easily. Old me never would've come to one of these; she was too scared. But the difference between then and now was that I had people to rely on, who I knew wouldn't abandon me. The music was better, too.

I was with Soph, like I had been for the past few weeks. We'd become so close that people actually started to think we were a couple; we weren't though. The two of us knew who we were and what our boundaries were. We were also the type of friends who just never grew tired of each other and thrived off being around one another. She was my safety person, and I was hers.

Everyone was back in the main area of the pub, dancing in the dark with a few strobe lights, something I didn't realize the pub was even equipped with, dancing to a mix between the worst top forty and classic rock. All the girls were dancing together, either rubbing up against each other or their partner while Soph and I jumped up and down like a couple of lunatics, screaming-singing at the top of our lungs.

The party went on until midnight when the bouncers started yelling at everyone to wrap it up so the bartenders could start cleaning up. The crowd booed for a while before eventually making their way out, some stumbling, some barfing, and some laughing at what must've been the most hysterical thing they'd ever heard in their life.

Everyone in the group located each other and we all began walking back to Pelican as one giant, sweaty heap. We took the usual shortcut through the woods to get back when Max, sans cigar, stepped back to join me in the back. Soph was busy talking with some of the other people toward the front.

"Hey," he said.

"Oh, hey, Max. What's up?"

He shrugged. "I just wanted to say that you looked really pretty in your dress tonight."

My cheeks grew warm with flattery. "Wow, thanks. That's really nice," I beamed.

He was looking down at the ground while he spoke, kicking a pebble around while he walked. "I've always thought you were a really cool person. You know, someone worth getting to know better." He chuckled to himself. "But it's silly to think that."

"Silly to think what?"

"That I could ever be more than just a friend to you." His hands were stuffed into his pockets as he walked. Whether it was because he was embarrassed, chilled, or both, I didn't know.

"Oh," I said, not sure of what to say next, letting the silence hang between us for a minute. "Well, I...I think you're an exceptionally nice person, Max. Really. There need to be more people like you in the world, and whoever you find next in life would be a fool not to see that."

He nodded, reluctantly accepting this answer. "I hope they do." Max turned to look at me again. "And whoever you run into next is going to be a very, very lucky guy."

I smiled in the dark at him. "Thanks, Max."

"Yo, we should hit up Osprey!" Derrick said in front of us. We had made it to the dorms' parking lot. "They're supposedly having this massive afterparty there. We should check it out!"

Everyone seemed to be on board with it, but really, I just wanted to slide into my extra-large pajama t-shirt and go to bed. "I think I'm gonna call it a night, guys," I said, walking toward Pelican.

"Me too," Sophia replied, following me.

"Same here," said Max.

Derrick stood in the middle of the street looking shocked. "What? But guys, it's an *afterparty*. C'mon, live a little!"

Dorian spoke up first. "Actually, I kinda wanna go."

"Yeah, me too," a couple of others agreed.

"See?" said Derrick. "They're coming!"

After a consistent amount of peer pressure, I was the only one out of the three of us who gave in. Sophia claimed she had to work tomorrow afternoon and Max claimed he drank too much at the pub and wanted to sleep it off.

I walked across the lot toward Osprey with the rest of the group, squeezing through the narrow entrance one by one and snaking our way through the hall, following the pulse of the music we heard thumping through the walls. Upon reaching the end of the hall, Derrick gave a good hard knock on the door so whoever was inside could distinguish it from the beat.

I was pleased to find Milo answering the door, the Colombian co-worker I reconnected with at the beginning of the season. "You all came!" he squealed, like he'd been expecting us the whole time. He had a half-empty bottle of vodka in his hand. "Come in, come in!"

We stepped inside, feeling intoxicated by just the smell of alcohol in the room. It was packed to the brim with people of various races, ethnicities, and cultural backgrounds. Some of them I recognized, many of them I didn't. One of them was a guy I'd met a couple of times who worked with Soph serving food in the EDR.

"Y'all came at a good time," he said, "this place is fuckin' *lit*, bro!"

Some kind of Latin EDM music with a deep, swinging beat was pouring from a Bluetooth speaker. Milo came around with cups, passing them out like candy and offering us shots of various liquors. When he got to me, he threw his hands around my neck and embraced me in a deep, affectionate hug.

"Lauren, how *are* you?" he gushed, pulling away to hold my hand inside of his.

"Hi, Mimi!" I shouted, remembering that he had told me to call him that last time. "You've got a killer party happening here!"

"*Thank* you," he said, cocking his head to the side while he looked at me. "Please, come. I want to show you something." Milo then pulled me by the hand into the crowd of people. I looked back to my group and noticed many of them had already started dancing, letting loose just as they had before back at the pub.

I felt my hand get dropped into another's that wasn't Milo's. I looked up to see someone I'd never met staring back at me with beautiful, dark chocolate eyes. Offering minimal instruction, he said, "This is Diego! He's going to teach you how to dance!"

I turned my head from Milo to this new person, attempting to hide my nervousness with enthusiasm. He was slightly taller than me with thick black hair and a strong, lean build. The sleeves of his shirt were rolled up to his elbows, and the top few buttons of his shirt were undone. His neck and collarbone glistened with sweat. Empirically, he was gorgeous. His chocolate eyes paired with his devilish smile seemed to offer a challenge I wasn't quite ready for. "So, you want to learn how to dance?" he asked over the thumping music.

I smiled, feeling spectacularly insecure. "Uh, well, I—I guess so!" I shouted back.

He grinned at this. "This one's called the bachata; you use your hips to help you."

Diego took my other hand, as well as the lead. His hips rolled from side to side in a way I'd never seen emitted from any guy before. Mine felt blocky and chopped up as I tried to mimic it. He was Patrick Swayze from *Dirty Dancing* and I was Baby, clunky and extremely unsure of herself.

I soon began to notice a pattern in his dancing. Diego shouted out rhythms as I started to catch on with each new motion. As the footwork began to work itself out, I started feeling the rhythm more than hearing it.

Diego threw my hands up in the air with his, above our heads, arching them out and back down, mirroring each other. Diego looked down at my hips, watching with pride my inner Latina come out, smiling bigger and wilder with encouragement.

By the end of the song, we were dancing like a dynamic duo. I let my hips curl out wider and farther than I'd ever allowed them to go. Diego pulled his leg out from between my knees that was initially there to support me and allowed me to continue feeling the rhythm with him. The skin on my forehead dampened with perspiration. I could feel some of the others looking over to watch.

When the next song picked up, barely missing a beat, Diego introduced me to something called the *lambada*. "This is known as 'The Forbidden Dance,'" he said, flashing another wide, devilish smile. Our hips swayed together in perfect unison. I stuck my butt out a little more this time, and soon enough, we were dancing against each other—my back against his chest.

I never did this type of dancing; grinding and twerking never suited me. But this had a reason behind it. I was learning that you couldn't dance like a Latina if you didn't have the attitude to go with it. I was in the middle of an opportunity to experience something culturally new and different, and it would've been a curse to let it pass.

More songs thumped through the speaker and Diego's and my dancing got so rhythmic that we began altering our height. Our hips would swirl their way down to the ground and back up again, the people around us whooping and whistling as we did it together.

Right then, I saw one of the girls I worked with in housekeeping point to me from the crowd that surrounded us and shout, "You are one of us now!"

I danced with about six other people that night. I had completely lost all sense of time and didn't care one bit that we'd reached the early hours of the morning.

The guy who worked in the EDR had been watching me enough to feel comfortable pulling me into him and started teaching me what he called "how to dance Black." He began to grab my hips and push them into him. "C'mon, girl!" he shouted. "Show me your moves!"

Reactively, I pushed myself away from him, shouting back at him, "Stop it! I'm not gonna dance with you!"

"What's wrong?" he asked. "I'm just teaching you how to dance right."

"I *don't* want to dance with you," I repeated, returning to my position in the middle of the dorm room. I surrounded myself with Milo, Diego, and about fourteen others, disappearing into the crowd to continue dancing the night away, unbothered and fully myself.

CHAPTER 33

········◆◆◆◆◆········

This was Dorian's last day of work. It was the beginning of the end for us all. People would begin their transition out of the park and back into to their pre-Yellowstone lives in the way Cinderella's coach turns back into a pumpkin. There were colleges to graduate from, jobs to regain, and life plans to implement. I think everyone understood this was the last time we would all be together in the same place ever again for, probably, the rest of our lives.

I had been preparing myself for this moment. I knew it was coming because I'd experienced it almost exactly one year ago. The people I'd met, the things I'd seen, the places I'd been, they were all their own version of Wonderland, and I knew the time was coming to return home after experiencing it all.

We all decided to meet at the Lake Lodge for our final hurrah. Dorian put out a final text to the group chat inviting everyone to join in if they weren't working, specifically requesting everyone who had one to wear their team jerseys.

The fireplaces were burning, the bar was churning out drinks, and the antler-ringed chandeliers hanging from the ceiling illustrated the epitome of an old Western ambience. The plan was to start at the Lodge before migrating to the employee pub just behind it. It was Dorian's idea to have us all illegally sign our names on the wood-paneled walls of the pub, an unspoken tradition alumni were secretly expected to uphold. This would be our quiet way of celebrating the friends we made and the adventures we had, while promising our future selves that we could continue to live on with lives of intention and fulfillment.

When most everyone had made it, Dorian directed our next operation. "All right guys, gather on the couch for a picture! We're getting a picture taken together!"

Fourteen of us pooled in together, collectively wearing our Aztec-patterned jerseys, for one final picture that would mark one of the most prominent moments of our youth. While that picture was being taken, I felt proud of every single person in the room for coming here, out of all the places in the world to work. But mostly, I was proud of myself for getting to do this whole thing twice.

I took on the mountains twice, scrubbed hundreds of toilets twice, made friends all over again twice, and got to live in Yellowstone National Park twice. I was so completely enamored by all the things I got to do twice.

For years, I had spent my nights hunched over the pages of my journals, pouring my heart's wishes and desires onto countless blank pages in an attempt to manifest a circle of like-minded individuals. It wasn't until now that I finally realized they were all waiting for me out here the whole time.

Although there was an unmistakable feeling of bittersweetness tonight, I couldn't help but feel that my only option was to feel gratitude—gratitude for the changes, the uncharted territory, the challenges, but most importantly, the belonging, both to myself and the park.

My impatient desires had at last been released like caged butterflies into the world, and I'd never seen such beautiful colors before.

I belonged here so wonderfully.

I belonged among the finer things.

ACKNOWLEDGMENTS

I have to be honest: getting this book off the ground was an absolute beast. Not only did the story demand to be written, but it took a herculean effort to get it to the point of even being *ready* for publication. For that, I have to thank Patti Fors, Sara Connell, and the entire team over at Muse Literary for taking a chance on this book and believing in it just as much as me. I appreciate you all immensely for that!

Next, I only think it's right to highlight my therapist, Trisha, for both obvious and not-so-obvious reasons. When I told her I wanted to become a published author over a year ago, she took me seriously and introduced me to Sara and her community. Ever since then, I've gotten to meet other writers, thought leaders, believers, and doers, and eventually publish through their community. Trisha, I'm entirely grateful for your support in every way, writing-wise and otherwise!

Lastly, I need to offer my deepest thanks to the ones who ground me: my family and friends. Mom and Dad, thank you for supporting my love of reading and writing from childhood to adulthood! It also probably wasn't easy to see your only daughter venture off into the middle of the Wyoming woods by herself, so I am thankful for your trust and flexibility in letting me become my own person in the way that I needed to. Nick, I am beyond lucky to have you as a life partner who supports all my creative endeavors and is always there to bounce ideas around with me (even if that means reading the first twenty pages of my nightmarish first draft). To my Yellowstone comrades: without you, this story wouldn't be what it is. Thank you for being a part of a small but impactful portion of my life. You will always hold a special place in my heart.

And to you, dear readers, thank you for taking a chance on a book that I hope becomes a small part of your own inner journey. Here's to experiencing the finer things in life!

ABOUT THE AUTHOR

L auren Erickson was raised in the Kansas City, Missouri area. She has a background in elementary education and moved to Chicago to earn a master's in educational policy from Loyola University Chicago in 2020. She worked as a book launcher for an Inc. 5000 company where she helped numerous bestselling authors release their own stories. Lauren currently lives in the north suburbs of Chicago with her life partner, Nick, in their renovated townhome. *The Finer Things Club* is her first book.

Printed in the USA
CPSIA information can be obtained
at www.ICGtesting.com
LVHW041939180724
785922LV00006B/140